Metal Oxide Nano[
Polymer Nanocompo[
Electronic D~~evices~~

Von der Fakultät für Elektrotechnik, Informationstechnik, Physik
der Technischen Universität Carolo-Wilhelmina zu Braunschweig

zur Erlangung des Grades einer Doktorin
der Ingenieurwissenschaften (Dr.-Ing.)
genehmigte

Dissertation

von

MARTA RUSCELLO

aus Rom, Italien

eingereicht am: 10.05.2019
mündliche Prüfung am: 31.07.2019

1. Referent: Prof. Dr.-Ing. habil. Wolfgang Kowalsky
2. Referent: Prof. Dr. rer. nat. habil. Achim Enders

2019

Dissertation an der Technischen Universität Braunschweig,
Fakultät für Elektrotechnik, Informationstechnik, Physik

Metal Oxide Nanoparticles and Polymer Nanocomposites for Organic Electronic Devices

The application of metal oxide nanoparticles in solution-processed electronics presents many advantages: they can be dissolved in organic solvents and used as printable inks, can be processed at relatively low temperatures and can offer increased stability compared to conjugated polymers. However, metal oxide nanoparticles also present certain technical challenges due to the higher surface to bulk ratio (e.g. electronic surface trap states) or present problems during film formation after solvent evaporation (i.e. agglomeration). For this reason, various kinds of polymers, from conjugated polyelectrolytes to insulators, can be employed to offer a hybrid solution to these issues.

In this work, three different nanoparticle:polymer systems are discussed as an interlayer in organic light emitting diodes (OLEDs) and/or organic solar cells.

In the first case, Poly(sulfobetaine methacrylate) (PSBMA), an air stable and solution-processable zwitterionic polymer, was combined with ZnO nanoparticles as electron injection layer in OLEDs. ZnO nanoparticles are widely used in organic electronics and thin film devices. Prominently n-type, this material is particularly interesting as interlayer in thin film optoelectronic devices. It is demonstrated that when combined with ZnO, PSBMA remarkably improves the surface morphology of the film but more importantly passivates its surface trap states, leading to more stable and better-performing devices.

In the second case, the improvement of the processability of NiO_x nanoparticle inks by blending with high molecular weight polyethylene oxide (PEO) is examined. Recently, NiO_x has attracted increasing attention as a promising hole extraction layer in organic and perovskite photovoltaics. This material offers excellent optical transparency, p-type conductivity and good electron blocking properties. Nonetheless, the fabrication of highly efficient NiO_x thin films is challenging due to the low viscosity of the inks and the high sintering temperatures of the precursor approaches. PEO can help to disperse the nanoparticles hindering their aggregation after deposition without compromising film functionality, as the presence of PEO is beneficial for a better tunability of the NiO_x film thickness and morphology. Also, when applied as a hole extraction layer on organic solar cells, PEO provides a tool for optimizing the electrical properties of the NiO_x film consequently improving device performance.

As the third system, ZnO nanoparticles were blended with polyethyleneimine (PEI) and used for electron injection OLEDs. The charge injection properties of the ZnO:PEI system are studied through ultra-fast pump-probe spectroscopy, giving new insight on the mechanisms taking place at the interface cathode interlayer/active emitting polymer in operating device conditions.

Metalloxid-Nanopartikel und Polymere Nanokomposite für Organische Elektronische Bauteile

Der Einsatz von Metalloxid-Nanopartikeln in der flüssigprozessierbaren Elektronik bietet viele Vorteile: Sie können in organischen Lösungsmitteln gelöst und damit als druckbare Tinte verwendet werden, bei relativ niedrigen Temperaturen verarbeitet werden und bieten weiterhin eine höhere Stabilität im Vergleich zu konjugierten Polymeren. Aufgrund des höheren Oberflächen-zu-Masse-Verhältnisses stellen Metalloxid-Nanopartikel allerdings auch gewisse technische Herausforderungen dar (z.B. elektronische Oberflächenfallenzustände) oder stellen Probleme bei der Filmbildung nach der Lösungsmittelverdampfung (d.h. Agglomeration) dar. Aus diesen Gründen können verschiedene Arten an Polymeren, von konjugierten Polyelektrolyten bis hin zu Isolatoren, eingesetzt werden, um eine hybride Lösung für diese Probleme anzubieten.

In dieser Arbeit werden drei verschiedene Nanopartikel-Polymersysteme als Zwischenschicht für organische Lichtemittierende Dioden (OLED) und organische Solarzellen diskutiert.

Im ersten Fall wurde Poly(sulfobetainmethacrylat) (PSBMA), ein luftstabiles und lösungsverarbeitbares, zwitterionisches Polymer, mit ZnO-Nanopartikeln kombiniert und als Elektroneninjektionsschicht in OLEDs eingesetzt. ZnO-Nanopartikel werden in der organischen

Elektronik und in Dünnschichtbauteilen häufig als Zwischenschicht eingesetzt, da sie *n*-typisches Verhalten zeigen. Es zeigt sich, dass PSBMA in Kombination mit ZnO die Oberflächenmorphologie der Schicht deutlich verbessert, vor allem aber ihre Oberflächenfallenzustände passiviert, was zu stabileren und leistungsfähigeren Bauteilen führt.

Im zweiten Fall wird die Verbesserung der Verarbeitbarkeit von NiO_x-Nanopartikeltinten durch Mischung mit hochmolekularem Polyethylenoxid (PEO) untersucht. In jüngster Zeit hat NiO_x als vielversprechende Loch-Extraktionsschicht in der organischen und perowskitischen Photovoltaik zunehmend Aufmerksamkeit erregt. Dieses Material bietet eine ausgezeichnete optische Transparenz, p-artige Leitfähigkeit und gute Elektronenblockiereigenschaften. Dennoch ist die Herstellung hocheffizienter NiOx-Dünnschichten aufgrund der niedrigen Viskosität der Tinte und der hohen Sintertemperaturen bei der Verwendung von Präkursoren eine Herausforderung. PEO kann dabei helfen, die Nanopartikel zu dispergieren und ihre Aggregation nach der Abscheidung zu unterdrücken, ohne jedoch die Filmfunktionalität zu beeinträchtigen, da die Anwesenheit von PEO für eine bessere Einstellbarkeit der NiO_x-Schichtdicke und -Morphologie von Vorteil ist. Die Verwendung von PEO als Loch-Extraktionsschicht auf organischen Solarzellen, bietet damit ein Werkzeug zur Optimierung der elektrischen Eigenschaften der NiO_x-Schicht und damit zur Verbesserung der Bauteilleistung.

Als drittes System wurden ZnO-Nanopartikel mit polyethyleneimin (PEI) vermischt und als Elektroneninjektionschicht in OLEDs verwendet.

Die Ladungsinjektionseigenschaften des ZnO:PEI-Systems werden durch ultraschnelle Pump-Probe-Spektroskopie untersucht. Dies lieferte neue Einblicke in die Mechanismen, die an der Grenzfläche zwischen Kathodenzwischenschicht und dem aktiv emittierenden Polymer unter Betriebsbedingungen stattfinden.

Publication List

Publications in peer-reviewed journals

- **M. Ruscello**, S. Stolz, D L. Gonzalez Arellano, F. Ullrich, S. Hillebrandt, E. Mankel, A. Pucci, W. Kowalsky, T. Emrick, A. L Briseno, G. Hernandez-Sosa "Electron injection and interfacial trap passivation in solution-processed organic light-emitting diodes using a polymer zwitterion interlayer", *Organic Electronics,* **2017**, 50, 384-388

- S. Schlisske, M. Held, T. Rödlmeier, S. Menghi, K. Fuchs, **M. Ruscello**, A. J. Morfa, U. Lemmer, and G. Hernandez-Sosa "Substrate-Independent Surface Energy Tuning via Siloxane Treatment for Printed Electronics", *Langmuir* **2018**, 34, 5964-5970

- **M. Ruscello**, T. Sarkar, A. Levitsky, G. M. Matrone, N. Droseros, S. Schlisske, E. Sachs, P. Reiser, E. Mankel, W. Kowalsky, N. Banerji, N. Stingelin, G. L. Frey, and G. Hernandez-Sosa "Nanocomposite of Nickel Oxide Nanoparticles and Polyethylene Oxide as Printable Hole Transport Layer for Organic Solar Cells", *Sustainable Energy & Fuels*, **2019**, Advance Article

- M. Casutt*, **M. Ruscello***, N. Strobel, S. Koser, U. H. F. Bunz, D. Jäsch, J. Freudenberg, G. Hernandez-Sosa and K. Müllen "Diketopyrrolopyrrole-Polymer Meets Thiol-Ene-Click Chemistry: A Crosslinked Acceptor for Thermally Stable Near-Infrared Photodetectors", *Submitted,* **2019** (*contributed equally)

i

Conference presentations (as presenting author)

- Poster presentation at **European Material Research Society (EMRS) Spring Meeting 2017** in Strasbourg, France, "Poly(sulfobetaine methacrylate) as solution-processed work function modifier and ZnO passivation layer in inverted OLEDs"

- Contributed talk at **Material Research Society (MRS) Fall Meeting 2017** in Boston, USA, "Beneficial Interactions between Metal Oxide Nanoparticles and Insulating Polymers for Interfaces in Solution-processed Electronics"

- Poster presentation at **21st Sede Boqer Symposium on Solar Electricity Production** 7-8th March 2018 in Sede Boqer, Israel, "Beneficial Interactions between Nickel Oxide Nanoparticles and Insulating Poly(ethylene oxide) for Hole Transport in Organic Solar Cells"

- Poster presentation at **14th International Conference on Organic Electronics (ICOE)** June 2018 in Bordeaux, France, "Inkjet printed Nickel Oxide Nanoparticles and Insulating Poly(ethylene oxide) for Hole Transport in Organic Solar Cells"

- Poster presentation at **Materials for Organic Electronics: Synthesis, Spectroscopy and Theory** June 2018 in Heidelberg, Germany, "Nanocomposite of nickel oxide nanoparticles and polyethylene oxide as printable hole injection layer for organic solar cells"

- Poster presentation at **Material Research Society (MRS) Fall Meeting 2018** in Boston, USA, "Nickel Oxide Nanoparticles and Polyethylene Oxide as Printable Nanocomposite Hole Transport Layer for Organic Solar Cells"

- Contributed talk at **Interfaces in Organic and Hybrid Thin-Film Optoelectronics** March 2019 in València, Spain,

"Beneficial Interaction between Nickel Oxide Nanoparticles and Polyethylene Oxide as Printable Nanocomposite Hole Injection Layer for Organic Solar Cells"

- Contributed talk at **10th International Conference on Materials for Advanced Technologies (ICMAT 2019)** June 2019 in Singapore, "Printable Nanocomposite of Nickel Oxide Nanoparticles and Polyethylene Oxide as Hole Injection Layer for Organic Solar Cells"

Table of Content

Preface

The present thesis was prepared within the framework of the Innovative Training Network INFORM project (European Community's Horizon 2020 Research and Innovation Program under Grant Agreement No. 675867) in the premises of Innovationlab GmBH in Heidelberg under the supervision of Dr. Gerardo Hernandez-Sosa, Junior Research Group Leader and Associate Fellow of the KIT, and Prof. Dr. Ing. Wolfgang Kowalsky, director of the High Frequency Technique Institute in the University of Braunschweig and scientific director of InnovationLab GmbH.

Since 2008, InnovationLab GmbH has been a platform for research and development in the field of printed organic electronics for universities and industrial partners. Its shareholders at the end of this thesis period include KIT, BASF SE, Heidelberger Druckmaschinen AG, SAP SE and the University of Heidelberg. All measurements carried out at another site are marked in the paper.

Contributions from collaborations to the results obtained in this thesis are marked in the relevant passages. The Photoelectron Spectroscopy results presented were obtained in collaboration with the group of Prof. Wolfram Jägermann from Technical University Darmstadt. The Infrared spectroscopy results were obtained in collaboration with the group of Prof. Annemarie Pucci from University of Heidelberg. As part of the Innovative Training Network, parts of the work presented were carried out during three different research stays. The Transmission and the Scanning Electron Microscopy analysis was performed during a research stay at the Technion Israel Institute of Technology, Israel under the supervision of Prof. Gitti L. Frey. The transient and the steady-state absorption and photoluminescence results were collected during a research stay at the University of Bern and Fribourg, Switzerland, under the supervision of Prof. Natalie Banerji. Part of the samples were prepared during a research stay at the Imperial College London, United Kingdom under the supervision of Prof. Natalie Stingelin.

This work was accompanied by a training network provided by the ITN project management, which provided further education in the fields of science, technology and management, as well as financial support. The Secondment Travel funds of the ITN project made all the aforementioned research stays possible.

Heidelberg, 06.05.2019

Marta Ruscello

You can experience the wonder of seeing them for the first time,
the thrill of discovery, the incredible, visceral feeling of doing
something no one has ever done before, seen things no one has
seen before, know something no one else has ever known.
No crystal balls, no tarot cards, no horoscopes. Just you, your brain,
and your ability to think.
Welcome to science. You're gonna like it here.
Phil Plait, 2005

1 Introduction

With the discovery of electric conductive properties of
polyacetylene in 1977 by Alan J. Heeger, Alan G. MacDiarmid
and Hideki Shirakawa that awarded them the Nobel Prize
for Chemistry in 2000, a new branch of material science was
discovered. Soon after that, the newly-born organic
semiconductors started to be employed in all the different
optoelectronic devices that were established technologies
in their inorganic counterparts, thus founding the field of
Organic Electronics. Organic electronics is a field of
materials science whose interest revolves around the
design, synthesis, characterization, and application of
organic small molecules or polymers that show desirable
electronic properties such as selective conductivity,
electroluminescence or the ability to generate current upon
illumination. One of the attractive benefits of organic
electronics is its potential low cost compared to traditional
inorganic electronics. Exciting properties of polymeric

conductors include synthetic tunability, electrical conductivity that can be varied by the concentrations of dopants, in some cases mechanical flexibility and high thermal stability. Furthermore, thanks to the freedom of design offered by organic chemical synthesis, organic semiconductor materials can be tuned to be processed from solution, a key property for enabling the potential high-throughput fabrication of electronics through established printing and coating technologies.

The first Organic Field Effect Transistor (OFET) was developed in 1987 by Torahiko Ando and coworkers, [1] and since then the optimization of this technology focused on the research of organic materials with high charge mobility and how to reduce as much as possible the contact resistance. [2] To date the organic molecules have reached field-effect mobilities ~ 20 cm^2/Vs.[3]

Organic photovoltaics (OPVs) were pioneered by Ching W. Tang and coworkers in 1986. [4] Since then, the run for the highest efficiency for organic solar cells has brought great interest on the development of broad absorbing, photoactive materials which have culminated in the first efforts of commercialization [5, 6] and current record power conversion efficiencies in the lab scale ~ 15.6%. [7] Compared to silicon-based devices, organic solar cells are lightweight, flexible, potentially disposable, inexpensive to fabricate (i.e by the use of printing techniques) and potentially with lower environmental impact. These characteristics enable fields of application in areas such as building integration, smart windows or wearable devices.

[8] Ching W. Tang and coworkers also reported the first Organic Light Emitting Diode (OLED) in 1987. [9] OLED-displays are now arguably the most established organic semiconductor technology. Ultra-high-resolution OLED displays are now available in the consumer electronics market with high brightness, extreme contrast, rich color rendering and long operational lifetime.[10] Furthermore, major advances in OLED technology are expected in the field of high-performance lighting, where improvements are still needed in terms of color rendering index, high efficiency, high brightness, and durability. [11]

A common feature of all these devices is that they require a multilayer architecture for efficient operation. This device architecture in necessary to energetically match the injection or extraction of charges from or towards the electrodes. The energy barriers at the interfaces of the device have, for instance, a large influence on the final device operational voltage, exciton recombination or separation efficiencies. In order to optimize the transit of carriers through these interfaces, the energy barrier between the Fermi energy of the electrode and the conduction band of the organic semiconductor must be minimized. In inorganic semiconductor devices, doping is a common approach for the fabrication of ohmic contacts. However, this is difficult to implement in organic semiconductors and is currently a topic or research. [12–14] One effective way to address this issue is to use charge injection/extraction materials between the electrode and the organic semiconductor. The presence of an interlayer in an organic electronic device not only has an impact on injection/extraction barriers, but also on the built-in field in the device, on the surface charge recombination, and on the surface energy.

In recent years, a large number of material classes have been investigated for their suitability as interlayers in both OLED and OPV technology.[12, 15, 16] For instance, alkali metals and low work function metals have been used as interlayers however they suffer from poor environmental stability limiting device lifetime. Organic interlayers based in small molecules such as TPBi CBP, and Liq are very efficient however their solution processability very limited.[12] In order to enable fully solution processed devices compatible with industrial relevant printing and coating techniques researchers have turned to solution-processable inorganic and organic alternatives. Self-assembled monolayers have been used to tailor the work function of metal electrodes however they require a precise deposition as multilayer or disordered arrangements are detrimental to their functioning.[17] Ionic materials such as LiF have yielded promising results however they can negatively influence the chemical stability of the devices due to ionic diffusion processes upon device operation. Most recently, conjugated polyelectrolytes and amine-rich polymer have been found to combine the qualities of the ionic materials and the SAM materials with easier processability.[18] The main drawback of these materials is that they require film formation as ultrathin layers as they usually do not exhibit good transport properties.[16]

Conversely, transition metal oxides are particularly versatile materials to use as interlayers, as they can be used to achieve efficient charge injection or extraction for nearly any type of electrode, combining as well solution processability and good optoelectronic properties. The first reported use of oxide buffer layers in OLEDs was by Shizuori Tokito and coworkers in 1996.[19] Now, transition metal oxides are heavily utilized in OLEDs, [20–22] OPVs, [15, 23, 24] and OFETs [25] as well. Transition metal oxides are components in many of the current record-breaking devices reported in the literature, including perovskites-based devices.[26, 27] Low work- function transition metal oxides, such as ZnO, TiO_2 and Al_2O_3 are used as injection/extraction layers for cathodes. Reversely, high-work function metal oxides, such as MoO_3, WO_3, V_2O_5, and NiO_x are often used as hole injection/extraction layers for anodes. Moreover, metal oxides can be processed from solution as a dispersion in organic solvents, allowing the formation of high-quality thin films through printing techniques.[28–30] Nevertheless, metal oxide nanoparticles often lack chemical stability, rendering them prone to exhibiting surface defect-induced resistances in organic electronic devices. Also, nanoparticles tend to aggregate; this phenomenon reduces their high surface area to volume ratio and subsequently reduces effectiveness. [31, 32]

This thesis addresses these technical issues by demonstrating that various kinds of polymers, from conjugated polyelectrolytes to insulators, can be employed to offer a hybrid solution by forming a nanocomposite with the nanoparticles and the polymers. Therefore, neutral, nanoparticle-based nanocomposite interlayers are the subject of this thesis.

In this work, three polymer:nanoparticle composite systems are investigated as interlayers in OLEDs and OPV devices: ZnO and poly(sulfobetaine methacrylate) (ZnO/PSBMA), NiO_x and poly(ethylene oxide) (NiO_x:PEO) and ZnO with poly(ethyleneimine) (ZnO:PEI). The processing properties of the different interlayers, the contact formation between emitter, interlayer and cathode and the resulting device properties are investigated. The results presented in this thesis provide new insights into the influence of the nanocomposite composition and morphology on their properties as interlayers, and consequently on the efficiency of the final device. As an important result of these investigations, it is shown that the appropriate choice of the polymer host with specific functional groups leads to the enhancement of the properties of nanoparticle interlayers, as observed for the ZnO/PSBMA and ZnO:PEI systems. It is also exemplified by the use of a NiO_x:PEO system that by appropriately dispersing the metal oxide nanoparticles into polymers, many of the shortcomings of their solution processing are overcome without compromising the inherent nanoparticle properties.

6

1.1 Outline of this thesis

This work is divided into a total of seven chapters. Following the introduction, **Chapters 2** and **3** explain the theoretical fundaments and experimental procedures necessary for understanding this work. Chapter 2 gives an introduction to the theory of organic semiconductors, and the working principles of OLEDs and OPVs while Chapter 3 discusses sample preparation as well as the utilized thin film and device characterization methods. Results are collected and discussed in Chapter 4 to 6.

In **Chapter 4**, the different of metal oxide nanoparticles:polymer nanocomposites are characterized as thin layers. Their electronic, optic and morphological properties are thoroughly investigated, evidencing that the polymers PEI and PSBMA interact with the ZnO nanoparticles by improving their interface properties and by passivating the nanoparticles defects, and furthermore demonstrating that the PEO acts uniquely as a sacrificial processing additive for the NiO_x nanoparticles. In **Chapter 5** all the optimized nanocomposite layers are applied as injection layers in OLEDs using a standard poly(polyphenylene vinylene) derivative as the emitting layer and their characteristics correlated to the device performance. In the case of OLEDs with ZnO:PEI as electron injection layer, the devices are studied through a specifically designed ultra-fast pump-probe spectroscopy experiment in order to give new insight on the mechanisms happening at the interface ZnO:PEI/emitter in operating device conditions. In **Chapter 6** the application of NiO_x and

NiO$_x$:PEO blends as hole transport material in different OPV devices is discussed. It is demonstrated that blending the NiO$_x$ nanoparticles with high molecular weight PEO offers a simple, low-temperature approach for the solution processing of NiO$_x$ interlayers which is also applicable for inkjet printing. In this approach, PEO is utilized as a processing additive, which improves NiO$_x$ film formation and was subsequently be removed prior to device fabrication. Finally, **Chapter 7** concludes this work with a summary discussion of results.

2 Fundamentals of Organic Electronic Devices

This chapter summarizes the basic theoretical concepts needed for an understanding of the measurements that are discussed throughout this thesis. After a short general introduction to organic semiconductors, excitons, free charge generation and charge transport in organic semiconductors is presented in Section 2.1, in Section 2.2 particular attention is paid to the interfaces in organic electronic devices, establishing contacts at organic/organic and metal/organic interfaces. In section 2.3 the properties of transition metal oxides nanoparticles and their functionality as interlayers are discussed. Section 2.4 deals on the one hand with the structure and the principle functionality of OLEDs and on the other hand introduces the most important parameters for assessing the efficiency of OLEDs. Section 2.5 deals with the structure and the functionality of OPVs and introduces the most important parameters for assessing their efficiency.

2.1 Organic semiconductors

The semiconducting properties of inorganic semiconductors are a consequence of their periodic, crystalline structure. Due to the associated potential of the atomic nuclei in the solid Bloch waves are formed, and the valence electrons are delocalized over the entire solid. This results in a characteristic band structure with an energy gap between the last fully occupied band (valence band) and the first unoccupied band (conduction band).[33] Organic semiconductors are solids whose building blocks are molecules or polymers made up by carbon and hydrogen

9

atoms and – at times – heteroatoms such as nitrogen, sulfur and oxygen.[13] In contrast to the inorganic counterpart, organic semiconductors can be divided into three material classes: Organic single crystals, low molecular weight compounds (often referred to as small molecules) and polymers. The synthetic tunability, the relative low cost of production and the possibility to process them from solution render these materials particularly interesting for the production of low-cost and high-quality electronic devices.[8, 34] This chapter deals exclusively with small molecules and polymers, as they are more commonly used in organic light-emitting diodes (OLEDs) and organic solar cells (OPVs). These materials are usually available in amorphous or semi-crystalline form and their semiconducting properties can therefore not be measured with a periodic potential and the formation of Bloch waves delocalized over the entire solid. Instead it is necessary to considerate of the electronic structure of the carbon atom, the basic building block organic semiconductor.

2.1.1 Conjugated π systems

The electronic configuration of the carbon atom in the ground state is as follows

$$(1s^2)(2s^2)(2p_x)(2p_y).$$

If carbon forms covalent bonds with other atoms, an electronic reassignment takes place and so-called hybrid orbitals are formed (hybridization). This maximizes the

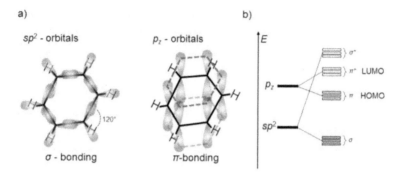

a) sp² - orbitals   p_z - orbitals   b)

σ - bonding   π-bonding

Figure 2.1: Orbitals of the benzene molecule as a prototypical example of an organic semiconductor. (a)The sp² orbitals of the carbon atoms overlap and form localized σ-bonds between the atoms. These are located in one plane and have an angle of 120° to each other. The p_z orbitals of the carbon atoms have only a small overlap and the forming π-orbitals are delocalized over the whole molecule. (b) Energetic position of the orbitals. The binding σ and π orbitals are fully occupied, the anti-binding σ* and π* orbitals are unoccupied. Modeled on [33].

overlap between the orbitals involved in the bond and thus the resulting bond energy. The so-called sp^2-hybridization of carbon is of great importance for the electronic properties of organic semiconductors. In this process, three new sp^2 hybrid orbitals are formed from the original $2s$, $2p_x$ and $2p_y$ orbitals, which lie in the xy plane and have an angle of 120° to each other. These three orbitals are each occupied by one electron, the remaining electron of the second shell occupies the $2p_z$ orbital.

When sp^2-hybridized carbon atoms form covalent bonds with each other, hybrid orbitals are formed between the atoms involved in the bond. The sp^2 electrons form so called σ-bonds, the p_z electrons form so-called π-bonds. This is shown in **Figure 2.1** using the benzene molecule as an example. In the case of the σ-bonds, there is a big overlap of the underlying sp^2 orbitals, and the electrons are very strongly localized between the corresponding carbon atoms. Therefore, σ-bonds make the largest energetic contribution to the total bond energy of the molecule. Conversely, the overlap of the p_z orbitals is very small and the electrons in the resulting orbitals are delocalized above and below the molecular level over the entire molecule: this is referred to as a delocalized electron system. Accordingly, the π-electrons contribute relatively little to the binding energy of the molecule and are energetically higher than the σ-electrons. The large overlap of the sp^2-orbitals leads to a strong separation into an unoccupied binding σ and an occupied anti-binding σ^* orbital with a very large energy gap. The weak overlapping p_z orbitals, instead, split up in binding π and anti-binding π^* orbitals with a much smaller energy gap than the σ orbitals. Therefore, they define the Highest Occupied Molecular Orbital (HOMO) and the Lowest Unoccupied Molecular Orbital (LUMO) with typical band gaps from 1.5 to 3 eV.[33]

HOMO and LUMO organic semiconductors can be roughly compared with the valence band and conduction band of inorganic materials. Similar to these bands, electrons can be excited optically from the HOMO into the LUMO and form excitons. Accordingly, the HOMO acts as a transport level for holes corresponding to the valence band of inorganic

12

semiconductors, the LUMO as a transport level for electrons analogous to the conduction band. However, the underlying physical processes differ quite considerably from those in inorganic semiconductors and are explained in more detail below.

2.1.2 Excitons in Organic Semiconductors

If a photon with sufficient energy hits an organic semiconductor, an electron from the HOMO can be excited into the LUMO. In contrast to inorganic semiconductors, however, as a result of such excitation there are generally no free charge carriers in the two energy levels, but the electron and hole form a bound state due to the Coulomb attraction, a so-called (Frenkel) exciton. The reason for this is the low relative permittivity ϵ_r of organic materials compared to inorganic semiconductors. While in the case of silicon $\epsilon_r \approx 12$ applies, typical values of ϵ_r in the case of organic semiconductors are 3 to 4.[33, 35] The relative permittivity of a medium is a measure of how well a charge is shielded due to the polarizability of the environment. The binding energy of an electron-hole pair resulting from the Coulomb attraction is proportional to $1/2r$ and thus more than one order of magnitude higher in the case of organic semiconductors than in the case of inorganic semiconductors. While in inorganic semiconductors the thermal energy $k_B T$ at room temperature is sufficient to separate electron and hole, this is not the case in organic materials and typical binding energies of excitons are 0.5 to 1.0 eV.[33]

13

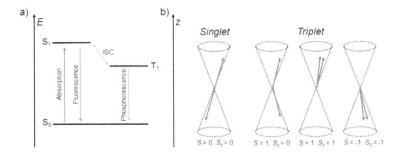

Figure 2.2: Excitons in organic semiconductors. (a) Electronic transitions, (b) Spin coupling duiing exciton formation. When an exciton is optically excited by the absorption of a photon, the organic semiconductor changes from the ground state S_0 to the first excited state S_1. If excitons are excited electrically, the spins of electron and hole can couple to a total spin $S = 0$ or a total spin $S = 1$. According to the multiplicity $2S + 1$ of the states (b), singlet and triplet states are possible, called S_1 and T_1. Due to the triple degeneration of the triplet state, 75% of the electrically excited excitons are triplet excitons and only 25% are singlet excitons. In fluorescent emitter materials, radiating transitions are only permitted for singlet excitons, i.e. from S_1 to S_0.

Figure 2.2(a) illustrates the optical generation of an exciton using a state diagram. An exciton is formed by the absorption of a photon and the organic material changes from the ground state S_0 to the first excited state S_1. Excitons can not only be generated optically, but also electrically. If an electron and a hole, which were electrically injected into LUMO and HOMO of an organic semiconductor meet, they form an exciton due to the Coulomb attraction. Both electron and hole have a spin of $s = 1/2$ and there are four possibilities how the spins of the two particles can couple

14

with each other when the exciton is formed, as schematized in **Figure 2.2(b)**. If the spins couple with a phase shift of 180 °, an exciton with a total spin of S = 0 is formed. Due to the multiplicity of this state of $2S + 1 = 1$, this is a singlet state. Such states are called S_k in state diagrams (S_0 and S_1 in Figure 2.2(a)). If the two spins couple in phase, an exciton with a total spin of S = 1 is generated. The multiplicity of this state is $2S + 1 = 3$, because the quantum number S_z, which describes the component of the total spin in z-direction, can assume the values 1, 0 and -1. Such states are called triplet states and are called T_k in state diagrams (T1 in Figure 2.2(a)). Due to the magnetic interaction between the spins of the electron and the hole and the exchange integral of the quantum mechanical wave functions of the two particles, the triplet states have a lower energy than the singlet state as follows.

In OLEDs, electrons and holes from the electrodes are injected into the device and form excitons in the emitter layer. If such an exciton is recombined, the released energy can be converted into a photon and the OLED emits light. This process is called radiative recombination. Physically, radiative recombination in first order can be described as a dipole transition from the excited states S_1 and T_1 to the ground state S_0. Due to quantum mechanical selection rules, a dipole transition is only permitted if the total spin S does not change in the course of this. The ground state of organic semiconductors usually has a total spin of $S = 0$. Therefore, the radiative recombination in typical organic materials in first order is only allowed for singlet excitons, i.e. for

15

transitions from state S_1 to state S_0. This process is called fluorescence. Triplet excitons may recombine exclusively non-radiating in first order. If singlet excitons exclusively contribute to light emission in an emitter material, this is referred to as a fluorescent emitter, an example of which are the emitter materials Super Yellow and F8BT used in this thesis (presented in Section 3.1.1). In the case of such emitter materials, the triplet excitons and thus 75% of the excitons formed remain unused and lead only to a heating of the device, which considerably limits the efficiency of the OLED.

Two types of emitter materials are known in which in principle 100% of the excitons formed can be converted into light: Phosphorescent emitters and TADF emitters (TADF, Thermally Activated Delayed Fluorescence). These materials were not used in the framework of this thesis. Phosphorescent emitter materials are based on maximizing spin orbit coupling through the integration of heavy transition metals such as iridium or platinum into the molecular structure. As a consequence, the radiating transition from T_1 to S_0 is spin-allowed and it results in phosphorescence. TADF emitters, on the other hand, are based on the minimization of the energy difference between S_1 and T_1. [36, 37] This causes the thermal excitation of the T_1- into the S_1 state (Inter System Crossing, ISC) both energetically possible and spin-allowed, so that these excitons radiate through fluorescence to the ground state.

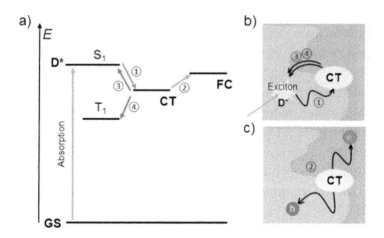

Figure 2.3: Energy diagram (a) and schematic representation (b-c) of the process of photon absorption and charge carrier separation at the donor-acceptor interface. The photon is typically absorbed by the donor from the ground state (GS) to the exciton hosting state D*, then the exciton propagates to the donor-acceptor interface, where it is separated via a charge transfer state (CT) in free charges (FC). From the CT state, however, the charges can recombine and be lost (step 3 and 4).

2.1.3 Formation and Separation of Free Charges

As already seen in the previous section, incident photons with the appropriate energy can be absorbed in the organic semiconductor and excite an electron into the LUMO of the material forming bound Frenkel excitons (electron-hole-pairs). Excitons are strongly bound, by Coulomb interactions (0.2 – 0.5 eV),[13] and by the low dielectric constant of organic materials. The high Coulombic attraction of an electron (e) and hole (h) leads to a broader

Coulomb potential well than in inorganic semiconductors. Furthermore, the e-h-pair binding energy leads to a strong localization of the exciton, which can expand over an entire molecule length. Conversely, the weak inter-molecular bonds cause that the electron's wave functions are spatially confined.[38] The exciton diffusion length L in an isotropic material is typically 5 – 10 nm and can be described by the diffusion equation as follows:

$$L = \sqrt{(\tau_0 D)} \qquad (2.1)$$

where τ_0 is the exciton life time; and D the diffusion coefficient.[39]

The separation of excitons is possible when its coulombic binding energy is overcome. This can be achieved for instance with high electric fields ($> 10^6$ V/cm).

This process can happen as well at the interface between an (electron) donor and an (electron) acceptor molecules with appropriate energy levels. Here, in an efficient and fast process on the timescale of 10-100 fs the electron located in the LUMO of the donor is transferred to the lower lying LUMO of the acceptor, and the energy necessary to break the exciton bond is provided chemically by the difference in the LUMO levels of the donor and the acceptor (**Figure 2.3a**). The charges at this point are still not free and are bound via Coulomb interactions, in the so-called charge-transfer state. The charge transfer state is the most prominent generation path for free charges, and as well of geminate recombination of electron-hole pairs resulting in charge generation losses (**Figure 2.3b**).

18

The charge carrier transport in organic materials differs strongly from the well-known band transport in inorganic semiconductors. Whereas the intra-molecular electrical conduction is defined by the delocalized π-electrons, an inter-molecular conduction is based on a thermally activated hopping transport of charge carriers between overlapping π-orbitals of adjacent molecules.[40] In comparison to the band model with valence and conduction band in inorganic semiconductors, the charge transport in organics can be described by a hopping model. It assumes an energetic density of states based on a gaussian distribution, where the mobility of charge carriers is dependent on the electric field strength and the temperature.[33] Therefore, organic semiconductors depict much lower charge carrier mobilities ($\sim$1 cm^2 Vs^{-1}) than their inorganic counter parts. An exception arises from highly ordered organic single-crystals, where mobilities up to 40 cm^2 Vs^{-1} have been demonstrated. [41]

The electronic limitations due to the strong exciton binding energies and the low charge carrier mobilities compared to inorganic semiconductors for organic materials changed drastically due to the development of fullerene derivatives and the invention of the Bulk HeteroJunction (BHJ) for the separation of the exciton in free charges.[33] The BHJ consists of a blend of acceptor and donor material, which typically forms in the deposited layer acceptor-rich and donor-rich domains. The interpenetrating phase-separated donor-acceptor network significantly enhances the exciton dissociation by a considerably increased interfacial area in

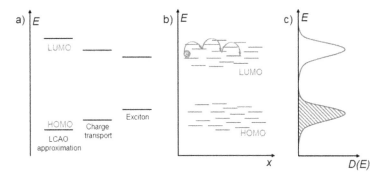

Figure 2.4: The energy gap of organic semiconductors differs depending on the physical process under consideration (a). As a result of the generally amorphous structure, organic semiconductors have a statistical energetic distribution of the HOMO and LUMO states by so-called hopping transport (b). For the mathematical description of the distribution of the HOMO and LUMO states, the state density D(E) *can be introduced, which approximately follows a Gaussian function with a width of σ =80 -120 meV (c).*

conjunction with domain sizes within the range of the exciton diffusion length.[35] So, after generation of an exciton followed by a dissipation into free charge carriers at the acceptor-donor interface, the charges drift via inter-molecular hopping processes to the corresponding metal-organic interface comprising a Schottky-barrier and contribute to the photo current.

2.1.4 Charge Transport

Molecular orbitals such as HOMO and LUMO can be calculated in a first approximation as linear combinations of atomic orbitals (according to the LCAO approximation, LCAO for Linear Combination of Atomic Orbitals) where hypothetically the molecular orbital contains only one electron.[33] The potential energy of the other electrons of the molecule is measured in a so-called mean field and interactions between the different electrons of a molecule are not considered. The HOMO and LUMO energy levels are therefore one-electron orbitals. For this reason, the energetic values of the HOMO and LUMO of a molecule can only be regarded as a rough approximation. Furthermore, the energetic positions of HOMO and LUMO are different, depending on whether the charge transport or the excitation of excitons are considered in an organic semiconductor.[13]

Figure 2.4(a) shows the energy gap between HOMO and LUMO for three different cases. The energy levels relevant for charge transport are lower than those calculated by LCAO approximation. The LUMO as transport level for electrons is below the value calculated by LCAO approximation, the HOMO as transport level for holes is above the value calculated by LCAO approximation. It has to be noted that in energy diagrams electrons can move freely downwards, while holes can move freely upwards. The reduction in energy can be explained by the polarizability of the environment. If an additional electron (hole) is introduced into the LUMO (HOMO) of an organic semiconductor, this additional charge interacts with the positively charged atomic nuclei and the other electrons of the molecule in question. This means that the charge is partially electrostatically shielded, and the energy of the corresponding energy level is reduced. The energy levels

21

relevant for the charge transport correspond to the electron affinity (EA) and the ionization potential (IP) of the organic semiconductor. Although the energetic positions of the LUMO and HOMO calculated by LCAO approximation differ from the electron affinity and the ionization potential of the organic semiconductor as just explained, both terms are often used synonymously in technical literature for reasons of convenience. In the case of excitons, the binding energy resulting from the Coulomb attraction must also be taken into account, which further reduces the energetic distance between HOMO and LUMO. Furthermore, due to the magnetic interaction of the electron and hole spins, the singlet and triplet states are energetically split, and the triplet states are generally at a lower energy (see Section 2.1.2, not considered in Figure 2.4a). In the literature, the electron affinity of a material is often estimated from its ionization potential and optical band gap, as rough approximation. [40]

In optoelectronic devices such as organic solar cells (OPVs) or OLEDs, the functional materials are amorphous layers. There is no long-range order in these layers and the chemical environment of the individual molecules varies statistically. This results in a variation of the polarizability of the environment and a statistical energetic distribution of the HOMO and LUMO states within the amorphous layer (**Figure 2.4(b)**). For the mathematical description of the distribution of the HOMO and LUMO states, the state density $D(E)$ can be introduced, which approximately follows a Gaussian function with a width of σ =80 -120 meV.[33]

The charge transport in organic semiconductors differs fundamentally from that in inorganic semiconductors. As a result of the periodicity of the crystal structure, bands exist in inorganic semiconductors and the electrons and holes are delocalized over the entire solid. As a result, the charge carrier mobility in inorganic semiconductors is very high, e.g. in silicon and germanium at 1450 and 3900 cm²/Vs, respectively. The electrons of organic semiconductors are delocalized within a single molecule or polymer chain and can therefore move intramolecularly almost freely. However, intermolecular charge transport is only possible within the framework of thermally excited "jumps" between localized states, which severely limits the charge carrier mobility in organic semiconductors. This carrier transport process is called hopping transport,

The associated mobility can be approximately described according to the Bässler model[33] as:

$$\mu = \mu_0 \cdot \exp(-C \left(\frac{\bar{\sigma}}{k_B T}\right)^2) \qquad (2.2)$$

Where μ_0 denotes the mobility of a hypothetical semiconductor without disorder, $\bar{\sigma}$ the standard deviation (width) of the density of state, C a calculation constant and T the temperature. Typical charge carrier mobility in amorphous organic materials is <10^{-2} cm²/Vs and thus many orders of magnitude below the mobility in inorganic semiconductors.[41]

In organic solar cells, the free charge carrier density is generated upon illumination and the carriers are collected by the electrodes where they have to be extracted. In undoped organic semiconductors, the charge carrier

23

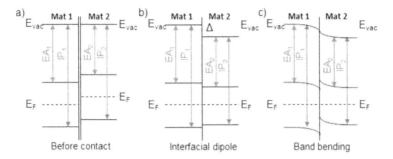

Figure 2.5: Contact formation at an organic/organic interface before contact (a), formation of an interfacial dipole when in contact (b) band bending in case of charge diffusion in the contact phase due to the associated change in charge carrier density (c). This does not change the height of the energy barriers for electrons and holes.

density is very low due to the relatively large energy gap of usually >2 eV and the large exciton bond energy. Therefore, in OLEDs the charge carriers have to be injected from the electrodes. The dominating process is called thermionic injection and is described in the following section.

2.2 Interfaces in organic electronic devices

The energy barriers at the interface of two materials have a large influence on the charge transport across the interface. If two materials are brought into contact, then in a first step the electronic alignment between both materials takes place and, according to the electron affinity rule, the electron affinities of the phases in contact determine the height of the forming energy barriers.[42, 43] In the case of organic/organic interface this is called Anderson behavior, in the case of metal/organic interfaces Schottky-Mott

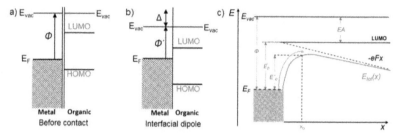

Figure 2.6 Energy diagram of the thermionic injection of charge carriers into an organic semiconductor. The original energy barrier E_b between the Fermi energy of the electrode and the transport level for electrons in the organic semiconductor is reduced to the value E'_b ($E_b - E'_b \sim 100 - 200$ meV) by the electric field applied during operation and the interaction of the electron with its mirror charge in the electrode. Electrons injected from the electrode into the organic semiconductor must overcome this energy barrier under thermal excitation.

behavior (discussed in the following sections). In the second step of contact formation, in case of a difference of the Fermi energies of the contact phases, a charge transfer can occur between the materials, where the energy barriers can change again.

Deviating from this very simple model, in reality there are often further effects at interfaces which directly influence the energy barriers forming [42]:

- Chemical reactions at the interface can have a direct influence on the electronic properties of the two materials and thus on contact formation;
- If an organic molecule has an intrinsic, microscopic dipole moment and has a uniform orientation at the interface, a macroscopic interface dipole is formed;

- Charged organic molecules or organic materials with free electron pairs can induce mirror charges in the electrode materials, which also leads to the formation of a macroscopic interfacial dipole.
- The wave functions of the electrons of an atomically clean metal surface reach into the vacuum. Therefore, the electrons of the metal have a certain probability of being located above the surface, which is associated with a permanent dipole. When an organic material is applied to such a metallic surface, the electrons are forced back into the metal, changing the size of the dipole. This effect is called push-back effect.

These effects are not considered in the discussion of contact formation in these sections but are discussed specifically in section 2.3 with regard to interlayer materials.

2.2.1 Contact formation between organic semiconductors

Figure 2.5(a) shows two organic semiconductors before contact. For both materials the vacuum energy E_{Vac}, the Fermi energy E_F, the ionization potential IP and the electron affinity EA are shown. The ionization potential and electron affinity approximate the HOMO and LUMO levels in the two materials.

If the two materials are brought into contact, according to the Anderson model the difference of the electron affinities (i.e. the offset of the LUMO levels at the interface) of the materials determines the height of the energy barrier for electrons. Similarly, the difference between the ionization potentials (i.e. the offset of the HOMO levels) at the interface of both materials determines the height of the energy barrier for holes. If the position of the Fermi energy differs in both materials, then in the second step of contact formation a transfer of electrons occurs between the two contact phases until a horizontal E_F is present. The prerequisite for this is that the material with the higher Fermi energy has occupied states in the Fermi energy range. Otherwise, a transfer of electrons from an energetic point of view is possible, but there are no charge carriers that could be transferred.

If an electron transfer takes place between the contact phases, the states in which the transferred charge carriers are after completion of the charge transfer are decisive for further contact formation. In principle, two cases can be distinguished. If interfacial states exist between the materials that the transferred electrons can occupy, an interfacial dipole is formed and thus a contact potential difference between the two materials is generated (**Figure 2.5(b)**). This causes a displacement of the vacuum energy at the interface and the height of the energy barriers for holes (E^p_b) and electrons (E^n_b) changes by the size of the interface dipole:

$$E^n_b = EA_1 - EA_2 + \Delta;$$
$$E^p_b = IP_2 - IP_1 - \Delta \tag{2.3}$$

Figure 2.5(c) shows the alternative case in which the transferred charge carriers do not occupy states at the interface but diffuse into the contact phases. This changes the carrier densities in the materials near the interface, which leads to a shift of the electrical potential according to the Poisson equation. As a result, the energy levels shift relative to the Fermi energy in the direction of the interface with the so-called band bending. The electronic alignment at the interface and thus the height of the energy barriers for electrons and holes is not influenced by such a band deflection. Both effects discussed here are frequently observed at organic/organic interfaces, as both an interfacial dipole and a band deflection can be present. [42–44]

2.2.2 Contact formation between metal and organic semiconductor

In solid-state physics, the work function is the minimum thermodynamic work (i.e., energy) needed to remove an electron from the Fermi energy level of a solid surface to a point in the vacuum immediately outside the solid surface. The work function is not a characteristic of a bulk material, but rather a surface (depending on crystal face and contamination) and is defined by the difference:

$$\varphi = -eV - E_F \qquad (2.4)$$

where $-e$ is the charge of an electron, V is the electrostatic potential in the vacuum nearby the surface, and E_F is the Fermi energy level (electrochemical potential of electrons) inside the material. The term $-eV$ is the energy of an electron at rest in the vacuum nearby the surface. E_F can be directly controlled by the voltage applied to the material through electrodes. Consequently, when a voltage is applied to a material, the electrostatic potential V produced in the vacuum will be somewhat lower than the applied voltage, the difference depending on the work function of the material surface. The fact that V depends on the material surface means that the interface between two dissimilar conductors will have a built-in electric field, when those conductors are in total equilibrium with each other (electrically shorted to each other, and with equal temperatures). [45]

Contact formation at an interface of metal and organic is more complicated in comparison to the case of two organic semiconductors. There are several effects that complicate the general description of the energy levels approximation. Among the possible effects at a metal/organic interface there is physisorption, in which the organic molecules bind to the metal through relatively weak interactions such as Van der Waals forces, and chemisorption, in which the molecular orbitals of the organic semiconductor shift due to strong interactions with the metal and has a great influence on the band structure at the contact surface. If a charge transfer occurs at a metal/organic interface, there is always an interaction with the mirror charge in the metal. By Pauli repulsion the wave function of the free metal electrons, which reaches out of the surface of the metal in a vacuum, is pushed back. The surface states of the metal are thereby influenced.[46] **Figure 2.6(a-b)** shows the case of contact formation by simple physisorption on a smooth metal surface. By physisorption of organic molecules the wave function of the metal electrons is pushed back, and the work function is thus reduced by the amount Δ to φ'.

29

For the potential barriers, this means that the electron injection barrier is smaller and the hole injection barrier larger than it would be calculated from the vacuum values. Depending on the type of absorption on the metal surface and the materials, this effect may be weaker or stronger. For gold electrodes, it has been shown due to this effect that the work function can change by 0.5 - 1.2 eV. [47]

From a more energetically detailed prospective, at a metal-semiconductor contact, the energetic misalignment between the Φ and the LUMO (HOMO) of the semiconductor, called Schottky barrier, determines a rectifying barrier for the injection of electrons (or holes). In **Figure 2.5c**, the energetic situation at the interface is illustrated schematically. In the case of established crystalline semiconductors this injection barrier is closed on the semiconductor side of the interface via highly controlled introduction of dopants, creating an ohmic contact. Unfortunately, this approach cannot be transferred to organic semiconductors. Figure 2.5c shows the contact between an electrode with a work function Φ and an organic semiconductor with electron affinity EA. In order to enter the LUMO of the organic semiconductor, the electrons must thermally overcome the energy barrier E_b = -EA. During the device operation, however, this energy barrier is reduced to the value E'_b, due to the externally applied electric field and the interaction of the injected electron with its mirror charge induced in the electrode. The total position-dependent potential energy of the electron can therefore be written as

$$E_{tot}(x) = EA - \frac{e^2}{16\pi\epsilon_0\epsilon_r x} - eFx \qquad (2.5)$$

Here the middle term corresponds to the potential energy, which the electron experiences due to the interaction with its mirror charge, while the last term considers the potential energy of the electron in the externally applied electric field F. If one determines by differentiation of this expression $dE_{tot}/dx = 0$ the maximum of the potential energy of the electron, $E_{tot,max}$ is at a distance of $x_b = \sqrt{(e/16\pi\epsilon_0\epsilon_r F)}$ from the electrode. With this the actually effective energy barrier is calculated:

$$E'_b = \Phi - E_{tot,max}$$

$$= \Phi - EA - \sqrt{\frac{eF}{4\pi\epsilon_0\epsilon_r}}\,e = E_b - \sqrt{\frac{eF}{4\pi\epsilon_0\epsilon_r}}\,e \qquad (2.6)$$

The relative permittivity ϵ_r of organic semiconductors is $\sim$ 3. If a typical value for the electric field in an OLED of F = 3 · 10^5 V/cm (3V externally applied voltage at a layer thickness of 100 nm) is used in equation 2.5, a reduction of the original energy barrier E_b by a value of approximately 120 meV is found.

During the injection into the organic semiconductor electrons have to overcome the energy barrier E'_b by thermal excitation. Without calculating the exact derivative, the injection current associated depends exponentially on the height of the energy barrier E'_b [33]:

$$j \propto T^2 \exp(\frac{E'_b}{K_B T}) \qquad (2.7)$$

Finally, it should be noted that contact formation is influenced by many factors and that, depending on the material, different and diverse states can form. At the same

31

time, however, this also demonstrates that injection barriers can be manipulated and that targeted material systems with the lowest possible potential barriers can be developed. For OLEDs, charge carrier injection is facilitated by the insertion of intermediate layers, and the same effect can be obtained in OPVs to facilitate charge extraction, as discussed in the following section.

2.3 Functional Properties of Interlayers

To maximize charge injection or extraction, the energy barrier $E_b = -$ EA between the Fermi energy of the electrode and the LUMO of the organic semiconductor must be minimized according to equation 2.5. In inorganic semiconductor devices, differential doping is a common approach to make ohmic contacts. However, it is difficult to implement this approach in organic semiconductors and a different strategy is used to extract or inject charge carriers. One possibility for this is the use of electrodes with low work function (for electrons) or high work function (for holes). In the past, alkaline earth metals such as magnesium, calcium and barium were used as electrode materials. However, these materials are very reactive due to their low work function, cannot be produced from the liquid phase and are oxidized by small amounts of oxygen and water, which affects the lifetime of the devices.[47] Furthermore,

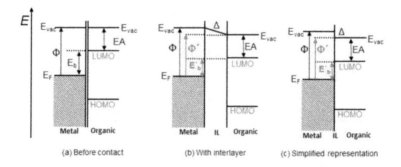

(a) Before contact   (b) With interlayer   (c) Simplified representation

Figure 2.7: Reduction of the work function of an electrode by an interfacial dipole. The functionality of many electron injection/extraction layers is attributed to the formation of an interfacial dipole between electrode and active layer. This effectively reduces the work function of the electrode and thus also the height of the energy barrier E_b for the injection/extraction of electrons.

it has been shown in the literature that monolayers of these metals can suppress the fluorescence of organic emitter materials, which limits the OLEDs efficiency. [48]

An alternative to this is the use of a metal with a larger work function in combination with an additional charge injection/extraction material between the electrode and the organic semiconductor. The presence of an interlayer in an OLED or OPV device impacts not only on injection/extraction barriers, but also on the built-in field in the device, on the surface charge recombination (particularly important for OPVs), and on the surface energy.

2.3.1 Fundamentals of organic interlayers

Recently, a large number of solution-processable organic interlayers have been investigated for use in organic electronic devices.[12, 15, 16] Some polymers, such as the conductive composite polymer poly(3,4-ethylenedioxythiophene)-polystyrene sulfonate (PEDOT:PSS) for hole injection/extraction, can intervene on the energy barrier with its own work function, that allows a lower energy barrier. The modulation of the energy barrier can be realized by introducing an organic Self Assembled Monolayer (SAM) interlayer with an intrinsic dipole at the electrode interface to control the interface energies.[44, 49] The model of the SAM effect on an electrode has been widely studied and it is with good approximation a model for many organic dipolar interlayers, as for example the polymers used in this thesis Poly(sufobetaine methacrylate) (PSBMA) and Polyethyleneimine (PEI).[50]

SAM molecules with a permanent dipole moment are used to adjust the work function of the substrate. Due to the uniform orientation of the SAM molecules in the monolayer, this molecular dipole moment $\vec{\mu}$ results in a macroscopic dipole moment $\vec{\rho}$ and it can be engineered to maximize its effects.[16] **Figure 2.7(a)** shows the energy diagram of a metal/organic contact without EIL between electrode and organic semiconductor.

Without EIL, the energy barrier for the injection (or extraction) of electrons is determined in a first approximation by the difference between the work function of the electrode and the electron affinity of the semiconductor. If a SAM is applied to the electrode as an interlayer (**Figure 2.7(b)**), the macroscopic dipole moment $\vec{p}$ leads to the formation of an interfacial dipole and thus to a displacement of the vacuum energy. As a result, the effective work function of the electrode and the height of the energy barrier changes to

$$\Phi' = \Phi + \Delta;$$
$$E_b' = E_b + \Delta \qquad (2.8)$$

In **Figure 2.7(c)** the contact from Figure 2.8(b) is shown again in a simplified representation widely used in the literature. Depending on the direction of the permanent dipole moment $\vec{p}$, SAMs can be used both to increase (hole injection) and to reduce (electron injection) the work function of electrodes.[51, 52] In addition to interface energies, SAMs can also change the wettability of the substrate surface. Changes in wettability can affect the film morphology which subsequently results in changes in the charge separation efficiency and the charge transport properties.[53]

2.3.2 Metal Oxide Nanoparticles as interlayers

Transition metal oxides are particularly versatile materials for use as buffer layers, as they can be used to achieve efficient charge injection for nearly any type of electrode. These materials can possess a wide range of work functions, spanning from extreme low of 3.5 eV for defective ZrO_2 to the extreme high of 7.0 eV for stoichiometric V_2O_5.[54] The first reported use of oxide buffer layers in OLEDs was by Tokito et al. in 1996.[19] Now, transition metal oxides are

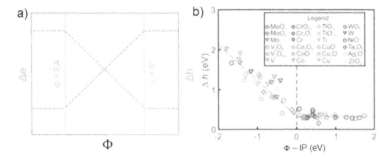

Figure 2.8: (a)An illustration of the energy-alignment trend for weakly interacting systems, showing how hole-injection barrier and electron-injection barrier depend on work function, ionization energy and electron affinity. (b) Experimental photoemission measurements of energy-level alignment at the anode interface for several organic semiconductors on numerous metals and metal oxides. Taken or redrawn from reference [55] (copyright under CC license).

heavily utilized in OLEDs, [20–22] OPVs, [15, 23, 24] and OFETs [25] as well. Transition metal oxides are components in many of the current record-breaking devices reported in the literature, including perovskites-based devices.[26, 27] Low work- function transition metal oxides, such as ZnO, are used as injection/extraction layers for cathodes. Reversely, high-work function metal oxides, such as MoO_3 and NiO_x are often used as hole injection/extraction layers for anodes. The following discussion was mostly derived from reference [55].

2.3.3 Electronic structure and Trap states

Many metal-oxide/organic interfaces are weakly interacting interfaces, in which there is no hybridization between the electrode bands and the organic orbitals. Consequently, there are no localized bonds and likely also no gap states at these interfaces. Energy level alignment behavior in these cases is mainly governed by electrode work function and organic donor/acceptor levels.[33] Weakly interacting interfaces give rise to perhaps the simplest energy level alignment trend, which is illustrated in **Figure 2.8a**. The horizontal axis is electrode work function, while the blue dashed line represents the electron-injection barrier (Δe) and the orange line represents the hole-injection barrier (Δh). **Figure 2.8b** shows experimental measurements of the trend.

Although transition metal oxides have been found to follow a general energy level alignment behavior, their diverse set of electronic structures affects their conductivity properties. Transition metal oxides can be dielectric insulators, defective semiconductors (p- and n-type) and metallic conductors. These properties are established from a combination geometrical, quantum chemical and electrostatic characteristics.[56] Although a quantitatively accurate description of an oxide's electronic structure often requires most of these factors to be considered, many of the qualitative features can be understood from rather simple models—such as ligand field theory—and by simply considering d-band occupancy.

In most metal oxides, the oxygen anions are arranged in an octahedral or tetrahedral geometry around the metal cation. In an electric field of octahedral symmetry, two of the five d orbitals are destabilized (pushed up in energy)

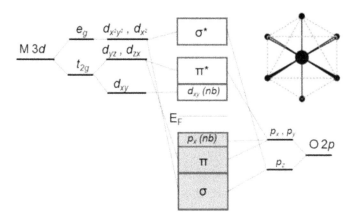

Figure 2.9: An illustration of a metal ion that is surrounded by point charges in an octahedral geometry (structure top right), and how the energies of metal d orbitals are split when octahedrally coordinated by negative point charges (in this case, oxygen ions), with consequent molecular orbital energy-level diagram. Redrawn from reference [55] (copyright under CC license).

and the other three d orbitals are stabilized (pulled down in energy), as illustrated in **Figure 2.9**. This splitting of *d*-orbital energies creates an energy gap. The two orbitals that are destabilized are assigned the point-symmetry label e_g, and the three stabilized orbitals are assigned the point-symmetry label t_{2g}.[57] Both O *2p* states and metal *d* states contribute to the total density of states. Overlap integrals between oxygen *2p* states and metal *d* states are usually nonzero, thus bands generally consist of a hybridized mixture of oxygen and metal states, so that in extended solids the energy levels are broadened into bands in the same way that atomic orbitals of metals and semiconductors are broadened into bands in solids, giving place to semiconductors, insulators or metallic conductors.[58] Without going into detail, the metal oxides used in this thesis all fall into the category of semiconductors.

Hypothetically, the Fermi level of a perfectly stoichiometric semiconducting oxide would sit at midway between the valence-band maximum and the conduction band minimum. Realistically, a perfectly stoichiometric oxide (that is, an oxide without any defects) cannot exist, as entropy requires that there will always be some finite concentration of defects. The most common defects in oxides are oxygen vacancies and metal vacancies.[59] In general, all of these defects give rise to either over-coordinated or under-coordinated metal centers and result in new occupied or unoccupied states near the conduction band or valence-band edges. These defect states make an oxide behave as either a p- or n-type semiconductor. Using the simplified ionic picture, one can say that coordination defects result in metal oxidation-state defects (that is, metal centers where the metal's oxidation state differs from the value it would have in the stoichiometric oxide). An oxygen vacancy would give rise to metal cations with an extra electron. The extra electrons occupy states close to the conduction band minimum, and thus can act as n-type dopants. Conversely, a cation vacancy would result in unoccupied states close to the valence-band maximum and can act as p-type dopants. In general, oxygen deficiency (or excess metal cations) makes an oxide behave as n-type, whereas metal deficiency (or excess oxygen) makes an oxide behave as p-type. As many of the oxides—due to intrinsic defects—are p- or n-type semiconductors, it is possible for certain oxides to be used as selective charge-injection layers. A selective charge-injection layer decreases the injection barrier for only one type of carrier—a property that is particularly important for OPVs, in which nonselective contacts result in high leakage currents.[15] Note that the actual position of a given occupied or unoccupied defect state, relative to the conduction and valence bands, differs from material to material, and in some oxides these states can act as traps.[60] In nanoparticles, defects and consequently trap states are known to be more frequent at the surface of the nanoparticle. [61]

2.3.4 Size-dependent properties of nanoparticles

In nanotechnology, a (nano)particle is defined as a small object that behaves as a whole unit with respect to its transport and properties. Nanoparticles are of great scientific interest as they are a bridge between bulk materials and atomic or molecular structures. The properties of materials change as the percentage of the surface in relation to the percentage of the volume of a material becomes significant. For bulk materials larger than one micrometer, the percentage of the surface is insignificant in relation to the volume in the bulk of the material, the situation changes when the object's dimension move towards the nanoscale, and by definition a nanoparticle has a diameter 1-100 nm.

Nanoparticles often possess different optical properties than the bulk, as they are small enough to confine their electrons and produce quantum effects, giving narrower and more effective radiation absorption or emission as in the case of quantum dots.[62] Metal nanoparticles are also known to undergo melting at much lower temperatures than the bulk material (e.g. for Au, 300° vs. 1064°C), which is useful when considering that sintering can take place at lower temperatures and in shorter times compared to bulk materials. Other size-dependent property changes include quantum confinement in semiconductor particles (as in the case of quantum dots), surface plasmon resonance and enhanced paramagnetism in magnetic materials.[63] In the case of metal oxide nanoparticles, crystalline phases with particular electronic properties that have low stability in bulk material are stable as nanoparticles. The size-induced structural alterations related with changes in cell parameters have been observed, for example, in nanoparticles of ZnO or NiO_x and many other cases, where the semiconducting nanoparticles could exhibit more distinctive insulator behavior for bigger particle size.[64]

As seen in the previous section, the most common defects in oxides are oxygen vacancies and metal vacancies, occurring especially at the surface.[54] The effect of such defects is enhanced in nanoparticles, as the big surface to bulk ratio renders it prone to exhibit a strong effect of its surface trap states, hindering the charge transport and lowering the overall quality of the device. The solution to this problem is proposed in this thesis by combining the metal oxide

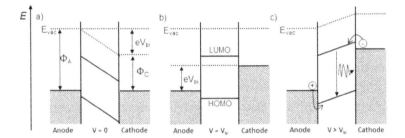

Figure 2.10: Schematic diagram of an anode-semiconductor-cathode transition at short circuit when the Fermi energy aligns. (b)No-load operation when the applied voltage corresponds to the internal voltage V_{bi} (c)Transition at forward applied voltage exceeding the internal voltage and charge carriers can be injected into the semiconductor, form excitons there and recombine radiantly.

nanoparticles with a suitable solution-processable organic material.

2.4 Functional Principle of OLEDs

In the simplest case, an OLED consists of an organic semiconductor, which is arranged between an anode and a cathode. As a rule, a "sandwich " structure is used, in which the anode, organic semiconductor and cathode are arranged vertically. During operation, holes are injected from the anode into the HOMO and electrons are injected from the cathode into the LUMO of the organic semiconductor. In the semiconductor layer the injected charge carriers form excitons and as a result of radiative recombination photons are emitted, that implies that one of the two electrodes must be (semi-)transparent so that the emitted photons can leave the OLED.

Since organic semiconductors have no intrinsic free charge carriers, the arrangement of anode, organic semiconductor and cathode can be described physically as a metal-insulator-metal structure.[33] **Figure 2.10 (a-c)** schematically shows anode-semiconductor-cathode transitions for different voltages. All three materials have a common vacuum energy before the materials come into contact or when the circuit is open. If the electrodes are connected by an external circuit, the voltage V_{bi} drops across the organic semiconductor due to the difference in the work function:

$$V_{bi} = 1/e \ (\Phi_C - \Phi_A); \qquad (2.9)$$

By applying an external voltage, this internal voltage can be compensated and in the case of $V_{ext} >- V_{bi}$ there is a current flow. Part of the charge carriers injected by the electrodes form excitons due to the Coulomb attraction, which recombine under the emission of photons. As described in the previous sections, non-resistive contacts are usually desired. By using special hole and electron injection layers (HIL or EIL), the energy levels can be adjusted according to the work function of the electrodes in order to achieve ohmic contacts. The injection layers reduce the potential barriers to the emitting layer and contribute to reducing the operating voltage of the OLED.

Electromagnetic radiation is usually measured by radiometric quantities, such as the radiation energy, which describes the energy of a certain number of photons, or the radiation flux Φe, which indicates the radiation energy per time. However, if the receiver of the light is not a technical

43

detector but light sources designed for the human eye, photometric units are used. The reason for this is that the receptors in the human eye have different sensitivities for different wavelengths. The conversion from radiometric to photometric units is done by weighting the luminosity curve $V(\lambda)$, which, according to the Commission Internationale De l'Éclairage (CIE), represents the sensitivity of the human eye to daylight. In low light conditions, the sensitivity to night vision changes $V'(\lambda)$. Radiometric quantities at fixed wavelength are multiplied by $V(\lambda)$ and a factor K=683 lm/W when calculated in SI units. From the radiometric radiant flux, the photometric equivalent, the luminous flux Φv, can thus be calculated with the unit lumen (lm) on the basis of

$$\Phi v = K \int V(\lambda)\Phi e(\lambda) d\lambda \qquad (2.10)$$

The luminance Lv is the relevant quantity when the radiation from a flat surface element $\cos(\theta)dA$, typical for OLEDs, is emitted at a certain angle θ from its normal direction through an aperture with the solid angle $d\Omega$ at a certain angle. The luminance with the unit cd/m^2 is calculated on the basis of:

$$Lv = d\,Iv/\cos(\theta)dA \qquad (2.11)$$

Where Iv is the luminous intensity in candela (lm/sr=cd) that measures the differential luminous flux $d\Phi v$ which is emitted into a differential solid angle $d\Omega$.

In the context of this work, if not explicitly mentioned, only photometric quantities are used. The optoelectronic characterization of OLEDs is performed by relating the photometric quantities to the current and voltage required to operate the devices. Specific parameters are thus determined, enabling a precise comparison between different emitting materials. The term efficiency is therefore interpreted differently. The current efficiency η indicates the ratio between luminance and current density J in cd/A. To compare the energy consumption of the devices, the luminous efficacy η_P is used, which sets the forward emitted luminous flux in relation to the required electrical power P. The luminous efficacy is expressed in lumen per watt (lm/W).

The turn-on voltage Von is defined as the value of the voltage required to reach 1 cd/m². The turn-on voltage can be used to estimate the internal field and injection barriers.

2.5 Functional Principle of OPV

Figure 2.11 shows the schematic band-diagram of a thin organic solar cell with the anode on the left and the cathode on the right. The donor:acceptor blend appears in the band diagram like a classical semiconductor with a "conduction band" with the electron affinity of the acceptor and a "valence band" with the ionization potential of the donor. The conduction and valence band edge are separated by the interfacial band gap $E_g = IP_{don} - EA_{acc}$. From the difference between the contact work functions and the charge transport band edges at the two contacts follow the contact extraction barriers $\varphi_A = IP_{don} - \Phi_A$ and $\varphi_C = \Phi_C - EA_{acc}$. As discussed in the previous sections, the role of the electron

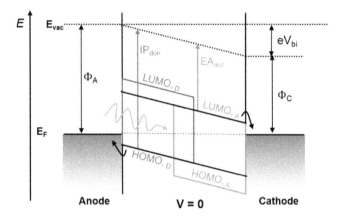

Figure 2.11: Schematic band diagram of an organic solar cell at V = 0V under illumination introducing relevant quantities like the built-in voltage V_{bi}, the work functions of anode and cathode, the electron affinity of the acceptor and the ionization potential of the donor. From the difference between the contact work functions and the charge transport band edges at the two contacts follow the contact extraction barriers.

transport layer ETL and the hole transport layer HTL is to minimize these extraction barriers.[13] **Figure 2.12a** shows an example of J-V characteristics of a solar cell in dark conditions (black curve) and under illumination (red curve). The electric power (P) as a function of voltage is also shown (blue curve). **Figure 2.12b** shows the diode equivalent circuit lent circuit, which describes the solar cell electrically. Without illumination (in dark conditions) solar cells act like diodes, that is they let current flow only if forward biased (when the anode is positively biased towards the cathode).[65] The photon generated current, dependent on the light intensity, is conventionalized as a

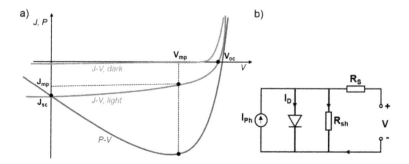

Figure 2.12: (a) Example of J-V characteristics of a solar cell in dark conditions (black curve) and under illumination (red curve). The electric power (P) as a function of voltage is also shown (blue curve). (b) Solar cell equivalent circuit.

current source parallel to the diode, which is the cause of the typical rectifying diode shape. The shunt resistance R_{Sh} describes the parallel resistance through the active layer and accounts for leakage currents, or shunts through the semi-conducting material. The series resistance R_S accounts for current losses arising from electrode resistances, supply lines and contact resistances. Internal parasitic loss effects can be therefore ascribed in a certain extent to these two characteristic resistances. The implicit function for the total current under illumination over a certain voltage range is derived from Kirchhoff's second law, as follows:

$$I = I_0 \left[exp\left(\frac{q(V+IR_S)}{akT}\right) + 1 \right] - \frac{V+IR_S}{R_{Sh}} - I_{Ph} \qquad (2.12)$$

In this equation the first term corresponds to the dark current, where I_0 is the reverse saturation current of the diode; a is the ideality factor and adjusts the influence of the different recombination processes; V_T corresponds to the thermal energy of 0.025 eV at room temperature. The second term describes the shunt resistance and the third term is the photon generated current. The shunt can be determined from the inverse slope of the J-V characteristic at the origin at 0V. The series resistance is calculated from the intercept on the y-axis of the derivative dV/dI.

Under irradiation, the electric power (P = JV) is negative, as shown in **Figure 2.12a**, indicating that the cell is producing energy. From the portion of the J-V characteristics lying in the fourth quadrant of the J-V plane, the photovoltaic parameters that describe the solar cell quality and behavior are derived.[66]

J_{SC} is the short-circuit current and refers to the generated photo current for short-cutted electrodes. V_{OC} expresses the open circuit voltage and ideally is derived from the difference of $LUMO_A$ and $HOMO_D$ of the OPV, as well as the Schottky-barriers at the metal-organic interfaces (see Figure 2.11). The energy level alignment of the anode and cathode work function is therefore of great importance for the power conversion efficiency (PCE). The PCE is defined by the ratio of generated electrical power P_{el} to incident optical power P_{in}, as presented in:

$$PCE = \frac{P_{el}}{P_{in}} = \frac{J_{MP}V_{MP}}{P_{in}} = FF \frac{J_{SC}V_{OC}}{P_{in}} \qquad (2.13)$$

where J_{MP} is the current density in A/m^2 and V_{MP} the voltage at the maximum extractable power (maximum power point, MP), as the power can be expressed as the product of the current and the voltage. The fill factor (FF) relates the area $V_{MP} \cdot J_{MP}$ to the area under $J_{SC} \cdot V_{OC}$ and serves as a quality factor for the diode shape. Being PCE dependent on both temperature and luminous incident power, solar cells are usually characterized according to a standard protocol, defined as: measuring temperature of 25°C; Pin of 1000 W/m² with spectral distribution AM 1.5G (sun at 45° from the horizon), corresponding to the standard 1 sun condition.

The procedure of the measurements carried out on the examined OPVs can be schematized as follows:

For the characterization in the dark, a potential sweep was applied to the solar cell in the dark, typically from – 2V to +2V, and the J-V characteristics was collected. The dark J-V characteristics give important information on the quality of the device as a diode (diode rectification, presence of pinholes, etc.).

For the characterization under 1 sun irradiation a potential sweep was applied to the solar cell, typically from – 1V to +1V, and the values PCE was calculated from the extracted parameters.

Lastly, external quantum efficiency (EQE) was measured for some of the OPVs examined. The EQE is a function of the measured photocurrent J_{Ph} at a known incident optical power P_{in} factorized by the photon energy hc/λ and the electron charge q. The photo current already considers all contributing optical losses (reflectance, transmittance, coupling losses) and electrical losses (recombination processes) and can be expressed as followed:

$$EQE(\lambda) = \frac{I_{ph}hc}{P_{in}\lambda q} \qquad (2.13)$$

49

3 Experimental Methods

After the theoretical introduction of organic semiconductors and organic electronic devices in the last chapter, this chapter deals with the experimental aspects of their preparation and characterization. Section 3.1 describes the production of single films of functional thin films as well as the preparation of complete devices. The following two sections introduce the analytical methods used in this thesis. Section 3.2 deals with the thin film characterization of single films, section 3.3 discusses the optoelectrical investigation of organic light emitting diodes.

The experimental work was carried out at the InnovationLab GmbH in Heidelberg. In addition to regular laboratories, a clean room of ISO class 8 is available there, in which the sample preparation and a large part of the sample characterization took place. In addition, some experimental work was carried out during research stays at the Imperial College London, United Kingdom, at the University of Bern, Switzerland and at the Technion Israel Institute of Technology, Israel. Results obtained in the laboratories there are specifically identified in the work.

3.1 Materials

In this thesis two kinds of devices are investigated: OLEDs and OPVs. In both cases, an active functional layer is sandwiched between two charge selective interlayers, respectively ETL or EIL in case they Transport or Inject Electrons and HTL or HIL in case they Transport or Inject Holes. The device is finally enclosed by the electrodes. For these devices two kinds of device architectures are applicable. The so-called regular architecture is defined as the sequence Transparent Anode/HTL/Active

Layer/ETL/Cathode and the so-called inverted architecture Transparent Anode/ETL/Active Layer/HTL/Cathode, as better discussed in Chapter 5 and 6.

3.1.1 Active Layers

In an OLED the emitter layer can be either a single material or a combination of a matrix and a dopant. For solution-processed OLEDs, both polymers and small molecules are used.[48, 67] Polymer films are generally easier to apply than small molecule films because polymers have better film forming properties and are less prone to crystallization. In contrast, the use of phosphorescent emitters or TADF emitters based on small molecules generally leads to higher device efficiency [20-23].

In this dissertation, a yellow spectral emitting polymer from Merck KGaA (PDY-132), commonly referred to as "Super Yellow" (SY), was used. This is a derivative of the polymer poly(p-phenylene vinylene) (PPV), whereby the exact chemical structure of the side chains is not known (see **Figure 3.1a**). According to the literature, the electron affinity and ionization potential of SY are approx. 2.9 and 5.5 eV.[68] SY was chosen as the emitter for several reasons. On the one hand, SY has very good film forming properties and spin coating makes it very easy to produce films with a high degree of homogeneity. On the other hand, SY is insoluble in highly polar solvents such as alcohols, which allows the subsequent application of a further material from solution. Finally, SY-OLEDs achieve a relatively high device efficiency

a)   PDY-132 (SuperYellow)   b)   F8BT

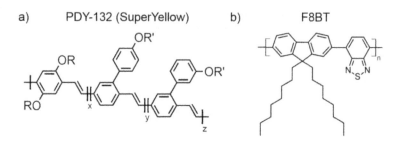

Figure 3.1: Chemical structures of the emitting polymer used for OLEDs in this thesis: SuperYellow (a) and F8BT (b).

for a fluorescent emitter, of more than 10 cd/A [92, 93]. In Section 5.2, devices using the emitting polymer Poly(9,9-dioctylfluorene-alt-benzothiadiazole) F8BT were produced as well (chemical structure in **Figure 3.1b**). F8BT is a widely used green emitting reference polymer in OLEDs.[69] The deep lying HOMO and LUMO levels (5.9 / 3.3 eV) make it air stable and is widely used for basic research purposes.

In OPVs, usually the active layer is composed by a donor material and an acceptor material. The materials used in polymer-based photovoltaic cells are characterized by their total electron affinities and absorption power. The electron-rich, donor materials tend to be conjugated polymers with relatively high absorption power, whereas the acceptor in this thesis is a highly symmetric fullerene derivative with a strong affinity for electrons, ensuring sufficient electron mobility between the two. As donor polymer, Poly(3-hexylthiophene-2,5-diyl) (P3HT) and Poly[[4,8-bis[(2-ethylhexyl)oxy]benzo[1,2-b:4,5-b']dithiophene-2,6-diyl][3-

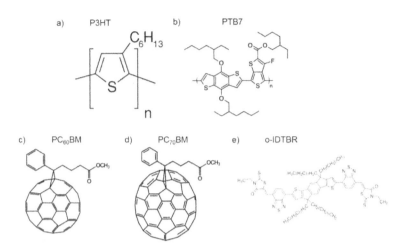

a) P3HT   b) PTB7

c) PC$_{60}$BM   d) PC$_{70}$BM   e) o-IDTBR

Figure 3.2: Chemical structures of the donor polymers P3HT (a) and PTB7 (b) and the acceptor small molecules PC$_{60}$BM (c), PC$_{70}$BM (d) and o-IDTBR(e) used as bulk heterojunctions in OPVs in this thesis.

fluoro-2-[(2-ethylhexyl)carbonyl]thieno[3,4-b]thiophenediyl]], more commonly known as PTB7, were used (chemical structures in **Figure 3.2a-b**).

P3HT is a semi-crystalline polymer with a backbone of linked thiophene units and hexyl side chains attached to it and it′s virtually the standard material for the research on OPVs.[8] The position between the sulfur atom and the alkyl chain is called head, and perfectly regioregular P3HT exhibits only head-tail coupling. The percentage of thiophene units that shows this coupling defines the regioregularity (RR), which determines the degree of structural order that can be formed in thin solid films. The regioregularity affects the mobility of electrons a in the polymer films and the overall HOMO and LUMO positions as well. In this thesis, P3HT (M_w = 72 800 g/mol, RR = 98%, HOMO and LUMO levels at 5.2 and 3.2 eV respectively). One of the most widely studied applications of P3HT has been for the development of organic photovoltaic cells based on solution-processed heterojunctions due to its low weight, flexibility and low manufacturing cost. The development of these cells is carried out with a mixture of (poly(3-hexylthiophene) and phenyl-C61-butyric acid methyl ester $PC_{60}BM$ (structure in **Figure 3.2c**, HOMO and LUMO at 6.0 and 4.2 eV respectively), the so called $P3HT:PC_{60}BM$. However, the extensive research and effort that has been made has not been sufficient because the power conversion efficiency has rarely reached a maximum of 6% with an average of 4%. [70]

PTB7 (1-Material, HOMO and LUMO at 5.1 and 3.3 eV respectively) gives some of the highest reported efficiencies for polymer:fullerene solar cells due to its extended absorption into the near infra-red and lower HOMO level, with efficiency up to 7%.[71] It is commonly used in combination with phenyl-C71-butyric acid methyl ester $PC_{70}BM$ (structure in **Figure 3.2d,** HOMO and LUMO at 5.9 and 4.0 eV respectively).

Recently, the non-fullerene acceptor material o-IDTBR **(Figure 3.2e)** has shown excellent electrical properties combined with high absorption coefficients, yielding record P3HT based solar cell performance of 6.3%. [72] o-IDTBR chemical structure consists of an indacenodithiophene core with benzothiadiazole and rhodamine flanking groups, with HOMO and LUMO at 5.5 and 3.9 eV respectively.[72, 73]

3.1.2 Interlayers

To optimize carrier injection or extraction, organic electronic devices contain an interlayer for electron transport to the cathode and a hole transport interlayer to the anode. A large number of material types are used (organic semiconductors, inorganic semiconductors, insulators) and the microscopic functional principle differs considerably depending on the material (as discussed also Section 2.3).[47, 74] In general, however, it can be said that interlayer materials minimize the energy barrier between the Fermi energy of the respective electrode and the transport level of the subsequent semiconductor. According to Equation 2.8, this minimizes the operating voltage required for a specific injection current or allows the extraction of the highest current possible. Furthermore, the charge carrier equilibrium in the devices can be optimized by varying the electron and hole selective interlayers. [13, 16, 44, 47]

Blocking layers on both sides of the emitter layer serve to minimize leakage currents and to spatially fix the recombination zone in the middle of the device. This is particularly important for OLEDs, because if the recombination zone is too close to the metal electrode, part of the radiative recombination is suppressed (quenching).[39] Of course, materials can also be used in OLEDs that combine the function of an injection layer and a block layer (see Section 5.2). In addition, interlayers lead to a planarization of the underlying ITO surface, which reduces the probability of short circuit formation in the device.

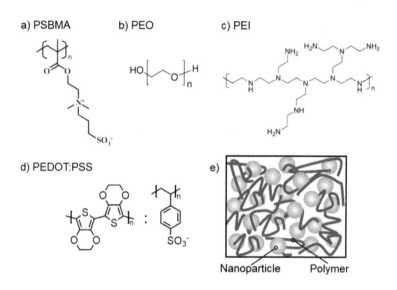

a) PSBMA   b) PEO   c) PEI

d) PEDOT:PSS   e)

Nanoparticle   Polymer

Figure 3.3: Chemical structures of the polymers used for interlayer fabrication in this thesis (a-d), scheme of the nanoparticle-polymer distribution of the nanocomposites used as interlayers.

The topic of this thesis is nanoparticle:polymer nanocomposites as interlayers. The employment of these interlayers in devices is discussed more in detail in the following chapters. The nanoparticles employed in this work are ZnO for electron transport and NiO_x for hole transport, both commercially available as dispersion 10 %wt. in isopropanol (Avantama N10, WF=4.3 eV) and 2.5 %wt. in ethanol (Avantama P20, WF=5.0 eV) respectively. Another transition metal oxide, MoO_3 (WF=5.9 eV), was employed as amorphous evaporated hole transport layer for inverted architecture devices. In **Figure 3.3(a-c)** the polymers used for the fabrication of the nanocomposites are depicted. Poly(sulfobetaine methacrylate) or PSBMA was synthetized by Prof. Briseno and coworkers [75], and has been used singularly and in combination with ZnO nanoparticles. PSBMA has non-conjugated backbone zwitterionic sidechains that create a strong dipole able to strongly modify the WF of the underlying substance. Polyethyleneimine (PEI) is widely known as WF modifier thanks to the dipole created by tertiary amines side groups and was used in this work in combination with ZnO nanoparticles.[18, 76] Due to the non-conjugated polymer chain, both PEI and PSBMA should be insulators. Polyethylene oxide (PEO) is a polyether compound with many applications, from industrial manufacturing to medicine.[77] It has already vastly reported that PEO has been used in OPVs as electron transporting interlayer, morphology-controlling additive and hygroscopic passivation layer.[78, 79] In this thesis, it was used singularly and in combination with NiO_x. All of these polymers are soluble in alcohols in order to solution process for the nanocomposite without disrupting the morphology of the active layer and allowing sequential solution deposition.

Figure 3.3e is a scheme of the nanoparticle-polymer distribution in the nanocomposite, a random distribution where the nanoparticles are dispersed among the polymer chain in a sort of "spaghetti and meatball" arrangement.

The reference hole-transport layer typically consists of a 20 to 50nm thick film of the composite polymer poly(3,4-ethylenedioxythiophene)-polystyrene sulfonate

(PEDOT:PSS) shown in **Figure 3.3(d)** and the suitability of NiO_x and NiO_x:PEO as solution processable hole transport materials is investigated. PEDOT:PSS has a transparency of approx. 90% in the visible spectral range and improves the hole injection from the anode into the subsequent emitter layer[80] as a result of its 5.1 to 5.3 eV work function. The polymer PEDOT is insoluble in the intrinsic state and has low conductivity. The addition of PSS leads on the one hand to a p-doping of PEDOT and thus to an increase in electrical conductivity.[81] In addition, the complex PEDOT:PSS can be dispersed in water and thus solution processed.

In this thesis Ca is used as thermally evaporated reference material and the suitability of ZnO/PSBMA and ZnO:PEI as solution processable electron transport materials is investigated. Although the term "solution-processed devices" suggests the complete production of a device from the liquid phase, for references Ca as electron transport layer is produced by vacuum sublimation. The reason for this is the high reactivity of Ca, which makes solution processing impossible.[82]

3.1.3 Electrodes

Transparent indium tin oxide is usually used as the anode material. This is an indium oxide (In_2O_3), which is n-doped with a few percent tin and, as a degenerate semiconductor, usually has a conductivity of 10 to 20 $\Omega/\square$. In the untreated state, the ITO work function is approx. 4.5 eV and can be increased to a value of approx. 4.9 eV with oxygen plasma by treatment from two to ten minutes. In this work, ITO is deposited on glass by the manufacturer and has a conductivity of 10 $\Omega/\square$.

The cathode is usually produced by vacuum sublimation through a shadow mask, typically using aluminum or silver. In this thesis silver was used for OPVs and aluminum for OLEDs.

If the so-called inverted architecture is used (depicted in Figure 5.1), the ITO acts as cathode and the Ag as anode.

3.2 Sample preparation

Figure 3.4 shows the layout of the devices produced in this work. Glass substrates with a size of 25x25mm^2 are used, which are covered with a pre-structured, transparent ITO electrode from the manufacturer. The various functional materials are then applied upon the structured ITO, and finally an opaque top electrode is applied. The area in which the anode and cathode overlap defines the active area of the device (hereinafter referred to as pixels). Each device has four pixels with a size of 4x6mm^2. The light emitted or absorbed by the pixels passes through the device through the transparent ITO.

The sample preparation can be roughly divided into three process steps and is described in detail below: cleaning and pre-treatment of the substrates; application of the functional layers; application of the cathode and encapsulation of the devices.

The glass substrates used are covered with a pre-structured, 190nm thick layer of indium tin oxide (10 $\Omega/\square$, Kintec), which can act as an anode or a cathode in the device

60

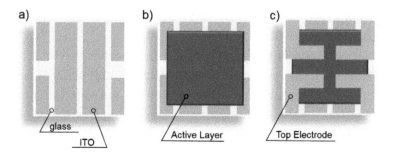

Figure 3.4: a) glass substrate with pre-structured ITO; b) with deposited active layer; c) with evaporated metal electrodes. The area where the electrodes overlap defines the area of the device pixels.

depending on the device architecture. In the first step, the substrates are cleaned with soap, acetone and isopropanol in an ultrasonic bath for 10 minutes for each step. Subsequently, the substrates are treated with oxygen plasma for 5 minutes. Plasma treatment is a further cleaning step and improves the wetting properties of the ITO layer. This is necessary to be able to apply polar materials such as the hole injection material PEDOT:PSS homogeneously by means of rotational coating.

The functional materials are applied one after the other over the entire surface through spin coating. Since many of the organic materials used are oxidized by oxygen and water, most materials are coated in an inert gas atmosphere. The hole injection material PEDOT:PSS, which is present as a dispersion in an aqueous solution, is processed differently in ambient air. After the application of one layer, the thin film is completely dried, in many cases with heat input, before the next layer is applied. Tables A.1

and A.2 summarize the processing parameters of the materials applied from the liquid phase as part of this doctoral thesis. Exceptions are the hole injection material molybdenum oxide (MoO_3), and the electron injection material Ca. These two materials are applied by vacuum sublimation.

In the last step, the cathode is applied, which in the case of the devices produced in this work consists of silver or aluminum. Both metals are thermally vapor-deposited in a high vacuum using a shadow mask.

To contact the devices, the anode contacts in the edge area of the substrates must be exposed. For this purpose, the functional layers above are mechanically removed. If the devices are to be characterized in ambient air, the active surface is finally encapsulated in an inert gas atmosphere. This is necessary to prevent oxidation of the functional materials by oxygen or water.

3.2.1 Spin Coating

Spin coating is probably the most widely used process for solution processing of organic functional materials on a laboratory scale. First, the functional material is dissolved or dispersed in a solvent is uniformly applied to the substrate, resulting in a homogeneous, bubble-free liquid film. The substrate is then set in rotation, typically at rotational speeds between 800 and 5000 rpm (rounds per minute). Due to the centrifugal forces, a large part of the applied solution is centrifuged from the substrate and the remaining extremely thin wet film usually dries within a few seconds. In the event that the viscosity of the solution is independent of the solid concentration of the semiconductor, the resulting film thickness d is:

$$d \propto c/\sqrt{a} \qquad (3.1)$$

in good approximation linearly proportional to the solid concentration c and inversely proportional to the square root of the rotational velocity a. Spin coating is very well suited for the deposition of organic semiconductors on a laboratory scale. In the case of most organic materials, homogeneous layers can be produced in the thickness range required for devices. However, spin coating is not suitable for the industrial production of organic devices, since very large material losses occur during the process, thus rendering it difficult to scale.

3.2.2 Vacuum Sublimation

Not all functional materials can be processed easily from solution. In many cases, for example, the electronic properties of the materials are influenced by interaction with the solvent (e.g. by oxidation). In the case of small molecules in particular, crystallization of the materials can also occur during drying, which prevents the formation of an amorphous film. One possibility to produce films of such materials is the so-called vacuum sublimation.

The materials are thermally heated in a high-vacuum chamber and sublimated. The gaseous molecules rise up in the chamber, condense on the substrate at the top of the chamber and form a film on it. If the materials are to be applied to the substrate in a structured manner, a shadow mask can also be positioned in front of the substrate.

In this thesis, films of MoO_3, Ca, Al and Ag were produced by vacuum sublimation. The setup used was a A MB-ProVap 3G evaporation chamber from MBRAUN. The system uses a two-stage vacuum system (scroll pump and turbomolecular pump) and the basic pressure is approx. $1 \cdot 10^{-7}$ mbar. A total of four voltage-controlled resistance evaporators (0 to 10 V) are available in the chamber, which can be used for the sublimation of metals, metal oxides and organic materials. The evaporation rate and thus the resulting film thickness is measured with the aid of two oscillating quartz crystals. These are piezoelectric crystals which are excited to a harmonic oscillation by applying an external voltage. If the mass of the oscillating crystals increases during the evaporation process due to the sublimated materials, this results in a reduction of their oscillation frequency. By taking into account the density of the sublimated materials, the deposited layer thickness can be precisely determined.

3.2.3 Inkjet Printing

Inkjet printing is a digital printing process commonly represented by the ordinary inkjet printer for home use. In industrial or scientific printers as many printing parameters as possible can be influenced. The interchangeable printheads are made of a chemically resistant material, which allows different solvents to be used for ink. The printing process can be controlled in detail via computer software in order to optimize the printing

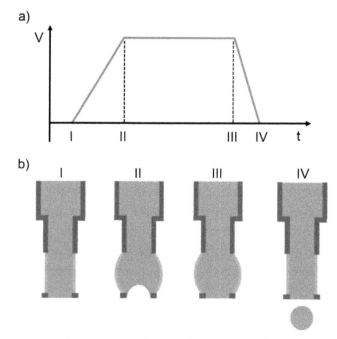

Figure 3.5: a) Waveform of voltage pulse to control the piezoelectric element in the printhead, b) Corresponding states of the nozzle.

result. The digital printing process is particularly suitable for structuring devices, as the layout can be quickly changed between the individual printing processes and individual design variants can be developed. In order to prove the scalability of solution processed nanoparticle:polymer nanocomposites, inkjet printing was used to manufacture these interlayers.

An inkjet printer works by feeding the ink from a reservoir into the print head. Depending on the manufacturer, this has a certain number of small openings, the so-called nozzles. At each of these nozzles there is a piezoelectric element that controls the release of drops that hit the substrate by oscillation. The print head itself can move freely over the substrate, so structures of any kind can be realized by controlling the exit time of the droplets. The piezoelectric element is controlled by applying a voltage pulse called a waveform. **Figure 3.5** schematically shows the profile of such a pulse and the corresponding states in the printhead. The voltage is first increased linearly, resulting in a negative pressure in the nucleus, as shown in **Figure 3.5 (I) - (II)**. This is followed by a holding time during which ink can continue to flow **(III)**, followed by a reduction in the voltage and contraction of the piezoelectric element, where a single drop is deposited **(IV)**. This is done on a time scale of microseconds $(10^{-6}\,\text{s})$. The duration of the rise, hold and fall times as well as the voltage amplitude can be changed in the software and must be re-defined depending on the ink to enable printing of the material. The example in Figure 3.5 shows a very elementary type of waveform.[83, 84]

In this thesis a Fujifilm Dimatix DMP-2831 was used, where the functional ink is filled into ink cartridges with an integrated print head with a total of 16 nozzles.

With the help of piezoelectric membranes, ink drops are formed in the nozzles with a volume of 10 pl depending and shot in the direction of the substrate during the printing process. The printhead moves in the x-direction and the substrate table moves perpendicularly in the y-direction to achieve a two-dimensional print image.

A very important parameter for influencing the quality of the printed image is the distance between the drops deposited on the substrate. If the drop distance is too large, not enough ink is applied and no closed film is formed. If, on the other hand, the drop distance is too small, the amount of ink applied is too high, which affects the edge sharpness of the applied film. For the layers printed in this thesis, the jetting voltage was fixed at 21 V using an optimized drop spacing of 15 µm. The maximum jetting frequency was set to 3 kHz, the print head temperature was set to 40 °C, and the substrate was kept at ambient temperature. The inkjet-printed layers were then dried in a vacuum chamber at $2 \cdot 10^{-3}$ mbar.

3.2.4 Encapsulation

If the manufactured devices are to be characterized in ambient air, the functional materials used must be protected from oxidation by oxygen or water. This is done by encapsulating the devices in an inert gas atmosphere. The central area of the substrates, in which the four pixels are located, is covered with a material with good barrier properties against water and oxygen. The outer areas of the substrate remain freely accessible for contacting the devices.

In this work the substrates were encapsulated with a thin glass plate (0.18 mm thick) fixed with a UV-cured resin (Delo Katiobond LP686). Since glass is impermeable to water and oxygen, the barrier properties of this encapsulation are determined by the barrier properties of the resin. According to the manufacturer, the rate of water permeation through a resin film 1mm thick is approximately 1.7 g/m². day (at 60 °C and 90% relative humidity).

3.3 Thin film characterization

3.3.1 Profilometry

The organic semiconductor's layer thickness in devices is usually significantly less than 100 nm. Tactile profilometry is suitable for measuring such thin organic films. A diamond needle scans the sample surface linearly and records its height profile. If a scratch is added to the organic layer perpendicular to the scanning direction of the needle and the organic material is removed locally, the layer thickness can be directly determined from the resulting height profile. The accuracy of this method depends on several factors, such as the quality of the scratch or the roughness of the organic layer. As a rule, however, organic materials with layer thicknesses >10nm can be reliably measured in this way.

In this work, a Dektak 150 Surface Profilometer from Bruker was used. In this system a diamond needle with a diameter of 12.5 µm is installed and the contact pressure of the needle can be varied between 1 mg and 15 mg.

3.3.2 Ellipsometry

Ellipsometry is an optical technique for investigating the dielectric properties (complex refractive index or dielectric function) of thin films. It is very sensitive to the change in the optical response of incident radiation that interacts with the material being investigated.[85]

Typically, ellipsometry is done only in the reflection setup. The exact nature of the polarization change is determined by the sample's properties (thickness, complex refractive index or dielectric function tensor). Optical ellipsometry exploits phase information (polarization state), so it's not diffraction limited and can achieve sub-nanometer resolution. In its simplest form, the technique is applicable to thin films with thickness of less than a nanometer to several micrometers. Most models assume the sample is composed of a small number of discrete, well-defined layers that are optically homogeneous and isotropic.

Because the signal depends on the thickness as well as the material properties, ellipsometry can be a universal tool for contact free determination of thickness and optical constants of films of all kinds, so that if the refractive index is known, the thickness of the film can be calculated. In this thesis the spectroscopic ellipsometer (SENtech Senpro) was operated at wavelengths from 350 to 1050 nm and angles from 50 to 70°. The complex refractive indexes were obtained using a Cauchy parameterized model with the help of the Sentech software.

3.3.3 Atomic Force Microscopy

Atomic Force Microscopy (AFM) is used to characterize the surface topography of solids. The sample surface is scanned with a metal tip and the topography of the sample is determined from the interaction between the measuring tip

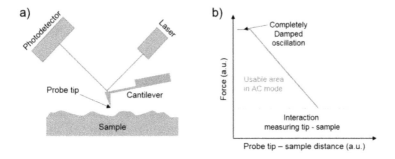

Figure 3.6: Principle of atomic force microscopy. Due to the interaction between sample surface and measuring tip, the cantilever undergoes a deflection which is measured with a laser detection system (a). In the case of the AC mode used in this work, the cantilever is excited to natural oscillations. Due to the force between sample and measuring tip, this oscillation is damped, and the topography of the sample can be determined from the damping (b).

and the sample surface. The lateral resolution of AFM measurements depends on the size of the sampled area and the diameter of the probe tip and is at best about 1 nm. The resolution in the z-direction is in the sub-nanometer range.[86]

In this work a DualScope™ 95 of Micro Engineering A/S was used. The measurements in this system are carried out in ambient air in contactless AC mode, using cantilevers with probe tips of <10nm diameter. The measurement setup is sketched in **Figure 3.6(a)**. The probe tip scans the sample parallel to the surface in x- and y-direction and experiences a deflection due to the interaction with structures on the sample surface. This is measured using a laser detection system and the topography of the sample can thus be determined. In the case of the AC mode used in this work

(**Figure 3.6(b)**), the cantilever is excited to oscillate at its resonant frequency and the resulting periodic motion is measured with the aid of the laser detection system.

Due to the force acting between the atoms of the sample surface and the probe tip, the amplitude of this oscillation is damped. In this mode, the damping is approximately linear to the distance between the measuring tip and the sample and thus the topography of the sample surface can be determined with high accuracy.

The RMS (Root-Mean-Square) value of the data points of the height profile is often used to quantify AFM images. This is a measure of the roughness of a surface, or the variance of the height profile. It applies:

$$RMS = \sqrt{\frac{1}{N}\sum_{i=1}^{N} z_i^2} \qquad (3.2)$$

Where N is the number of all data points and z_i the difference of the i-th data point from the average height of all points.

3.3.4 Scanning Electron Microscopy

In scanning electron microscopy (SEM), electrons are accelerated at a voltage of 8 - 30 kV and focused into a beam. With this beam the sample is scanned point by point. The most common imaging mode collects low-energy (< 50 eV) secondary electrons that are ejected from conduction or valence bands of the specimen atoms by inelastic scattering interactions with beam electrons. Due to their low energy, these electrons originate from within a few nanometers below the sample surface. The brightness of the signal depends on the number of secondary electrons reaching the detector. Steep surfaces and edges tend to be brighter than flat surfaces, which results in images with a well-defined, three-dimensional appearance. Using the signal of secondary electrons image resolution less than 0.5 nm is possible.[87]

Backscattered electrons (BSE) consist of high-energy electrons originating in the electron beam, that are reflected or back-scattered out of the specimen interaction volume by elastic scattering interactions with specimen atoms. Since heavy elements (high atomic number) backscatter electrons more strongly than light elements (low atomic number), and thus appear brighter in the image, BSEs are used to detect contrast between areas with different chemical compositions.

SEM images were collected with the help of Artem Levitsky from Prof. G. Frey's group in Technion Israel Institute of Technology. High-resolution top view SEM images were obtained using the Zeiss Ultra Plus high-resolution scanning electron microscope (HRSEM), equipped with a Schottky field emission electron source. The images were acquired using both secondary electrons and backscattered electrons detectors, at an accelerating voltage of 2 kV and at a working distance of ~3.5 mm. Samples were prepared by spin-coating on silicon wafer substrates.

Energy-dispersive X-ray spectroscopy (EDS) is an analytical technique used for the elemental analysis, i.e. to determine which chemical elements are present in a sample and can be used to estimate their relative abundance. It relies on an interaction of some source of X-ray excitation (the electron beam from the SEM) and the sample. Combining the X-Ray spectroscopy with the scanning electron microscopy allows the mapping of chemical elements densities in a sample.[88] The EDS mapping in this thesis were performed at 4 kV accelerating voltage and at 6.5 mm working distance. The EDS measurements were conducted with K_α and L_α signals of carbon and nickel, respectively. The samples were fabricated with a thickness of 400 nm for instrumental accuracy.

3.3.5 Transmission Electron Microscopy

Transmission Electron Microscopy is a microscopy technique in which a beam of electrons is transmitted through a specimen to form an image. The specimen in this work is a suspension on a copper grid. An image is formed from the interaction of the electrons with the sample as the beam is transmitted through the specimen.[89] The image is then magnified and focused onto a scintillator attached to a charge-coupled device. To increase the mean free path of the electron gas interaction, a standard TEM is evacuated to low pressures, typically on the order of 10^{-9} mbar. If the objective aperture is small enough to limit the angle of acceptance to smaller values than the Bragg angle for all scattered electrons, a bright-field shadow projection is obtained, imaging only the intensity variations of the electron beam current transmitted by the specimen, which was the case of the images collected for this thesis. TEM images were collected with the help of Tanmoy Sarkar from

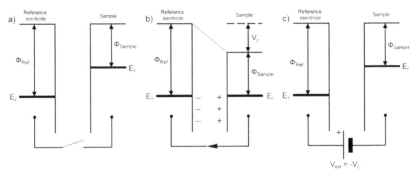

Figure 3.7: Measuring principle of a Kelvin probe. Reference electrode and sample form a plate capacitor (a). If both materials are brought into electrical contact, electrons are transferred, and the Fermi energies are equalized. This results in a contact voltage V_C between reference electrode and sample (b). By applying an external voltage V_{ext} of the appropriate magnitude, the capacitor can be discharged again and $V_{ext} = -(\Phi_{Ref} - \Phi_{Sample})$ (c) applies. Redrawn from [45].

Prof. G. Frey's group in Technion Israel Institute of Technology, using a FEI Tecnai T20 system with a LaB$_6$ electron source, operated at a working voltage of 200 kV.

3.3.6 Kelvin Probe

With the help of Kelvin probe measurements, the work function of conductive and semiconductive materials can be determined. This is a relative measurement in which the work function between the sample to be investigated and a reference electrode is determined, i.e. in order to determine the absolute value of the work function of the sample, a reference sample of known work function must also be measured. In the following, the underlying measuring principle is briefly explained. For a comprehensive introduction, a look at the corresponding technical literature is recommended [45].

A typical Kelvin probe setup consists of a flat circular reference electrode located directly above the sample to be investigated. In this arrangement the reference electrode and sample surface form a plate capacitor in combination with the ambient air as insulator. If the reference electrode and sample are conductively connected to each other, a transfer of electrons occurs and both materials (capacitor plates) are electrically charged if the work function of the two materials differs (**Figure 3.7(a) and (b)**). As a result, a contact voltage $V_C = \Phi_{Ref} - \Phi_{Sample}$ is applied between the materials, the size of which is determined by the difference of the work function. During the measurement, the distance between reference electrode and sample is periodically varied. This results in a current flow between the reference electrode and the sample, which is used to determine the work function difference between the two materials. To determine the work function difference $\Phi_{Ref} - \Phi_{Sample}$, an external voltage V_{ext} is applied so that the charge on the capacitor plates (reference electrode and sample) and thus this current flow becomes zero, as shown in **Figure 3.4(c)**, so that $V_{ext} = -V_C = -(\Phi_{Ref} - \Phi_{Sample})$. For the Kelvin probe measurements carried out in this work, a setup from KP Technology was used. This is located in ambient air and is equipped with a gold reference electrode with an area of 2 mm^2.

3.3.7 Photoelectron Spectroscopy

In addition to Kelvin probe measurements, photoelectron spectroscopy (PES) is used in this thesis to investigate the contact formation between electrode, interlayer and active layer. PES is based on the external photoelectric effect, according to which photons of sufficiently high energy can release electrons from solids. By comparing the kinetic energy of such electrons with the energy of the exciting photons, the original binding energy of the electrons in the solid can be determined. Because the energy of an X-ray with particular wavelength is known (in this case a Al K_α X-rays, $h\nu$ = 1486.6 eV), and because the emitted electrons' kinetic energies are measured, the electron binding energy of each of the emitted electrons can be determined by using the equation:

$$E_{binding} = h\nu - (E_{kinetic} + \Phi) \qquad (3.3)$$

where $E_{binding}$ is the binding energy of the electron, $h\nu$ is the energy of the X-ray photons being used, $E_{kinetic}$ is the kinetic energy of the electron as measured by the instrument and Φ is the work function dependent on both the spectrometer and the material.[46] This equation is essentially a conservation of energy equation.

The output of the measurement is usually a survey spectrum of the binding energies measured where all the elements present in the sample surface have an emission peak (see e.g. Figure 4.3). All occurring emission lines can be clearly assigned to the different elements present in the sample on the basis of the binding energy.

In addition to the identification of the elements present in a material, XPS measurements also provide information about the stoichiometric ratio in which these elements are present in the sample examined. By taking into account the atomic sensitivity factors (i.e. sensitivity of the detector, mean free path of the photoelectrons and depth of photoionization), the relative chemical composition of the sample can be inferred from the intensity ratio of the core level lines alone.

A measurement of the work function of the sample can be performed by PES. According to equation 3.2.3, the binding energy of the most strongly bound electrons, which can just leave the sample by absorption of a photon, is as follows

$$E_{bin,\,max} = h\nu - \Phi_{Sample} \qquad (3.4)$$

Above this binding energy, the intensity of the spectrum drops to zero because the photon energy is no longer sufficient to release electrons from the sample. Coming from lower binding energies, the intensity of the signal usually increases strongly up to this binding energy. The reason for this is that many secondary electrons, i.e. inelastically scattered electrons, are detected in this region of the spectrum. In this context, one speaks of the so-called secondary electron edge (see e.g. Figure 4.4). According to equation 3.4, the difference between the photon energy and the position of the secondary electron edge can be used to calculate the work function of the sample. It must be considered that the photoelectrons at the secondary electron edge have a kinetic energy of $E_{kin} = 0$ after leaving the sample and thus cannot actually reach the analyzer. In order to detect them nevertheless, an electric field is applied between the sample and the spectrometer, which accelerates the electrons in the direction of the analyzer. When evaluating the data, the resulting spectra must be corrected accordingly.

If an adsorbate layer is applied to a substrate material, some of the electrons emitted by the substrate are scattered inelastically in the adsorbate layer and the intensity of the substrate emissions decreases as a result. The thickness of a thin layer can be calculated by the damping of the core level energy of the substrate, according to the equation

$$d = \lambda \ln(I_0/I) \qquad (3.5)$$

Where d is the thickness, λ corresponds to the mean free path length of electrons in the adsorbate layer (which generally depends on their kinetic energy) and I_0 and I are the emission intensity of the substrate and the substrate covered by the adsorbate respectively. This is only valid in the case of a closed adsorbate layer with homogeneous layer thickness. The mean free path length of electrons in solids is very small and typical values are between minimum 5 and maximum 25Å [90] depending on the kinetic energy of the photoelectrons. Because of this, photoelectron spectroscopy is very surface sensitive. The information depth of PES measurements is about 3 - 5 times the mean free path length, which usually corresponds to ~ 10nm.

The setup used for this is thesis is in the *Clustertool* at InnovationLab and belongs to the working group of Prof. W. Jägermann at the Technical University of Darmstadt.

Measurements were conducted and elaborated by Florian Ullrich and Patrick Reiser. The photoelectron spectrometer PHI VersaProbe II of Physical Electronics used in this work contains as photon source both an X-ray tube and a UV gas discharge lamp. Depending on the photon source used, a monochromatized Al K_α X-ray source and an Omicron HIS 13-helium discharge lamp, one can speak of XPS (X-ray Photoelectron Spectroscopy) or UPS (Ultraviolet Photoelectron Spectroscopy) respectively. The photoelectrons emitted by the sample are detected in a spherical hemispherical analyzer.

3.3.8 Infrared Spectroscopy

With the energy of photons in the mid-IR range, bonds in organic molecules can be excited. Such vibrations represent fingerprints of the molecules and their dielectric background and can hence be used to identify molecular species. In addition to molecular vibrations, states in the bandgap of charged polymers can be electronically excited in this spectral region. A detailed description can be found in [91]. The setup used for this is thesis is in the *Clustertool* at InnovationLab and belongs to the working group of Prof. A. Pucci's at the University of Heidelberg. Measurements were conducted and elaborated by Sabina Hillebrandt. Fourier Transform Infrared Reflection Absorption Spectroscopy (FT-IRRAS) measurements were obtained in the nitrogen purged sample compartment of a Bruker Vertex80v Fourier-transform (FT) IR spectrometer using p-polarized light and an angle of incidence of 75° with respect to the surface normal. A liquid nitrogen cooled mercury cadmium telluride (MCT) detector was used and all spectra are the average over 200 scans that were taken with a resolution of 4 cm^{-1}. To eliminate influences of the setup and to distinguish between the material that is investigated and the substrate, the recorded spectrum is divided by a reference spectrum of a bare substrate.

3.3.9 Optical Spectroscopy

The optical band gap of organic semiconductors is typically between 1.5 and 3.5 eV and thus in the visible or near UV range. If an organic semiconductor with a typical layer thickness is irradiated with UV or visible (Vis) light, some of the photons are absorbed. The spectral measurement of this absorption provides information about the optical band gap of the material.

In the context of this work a UV-Vis absorption spectrometer of the company Avantes was used. In this system, the measurement is carried out in transmission, with the sample being measured is positioned between two glass fibers. A combined deuterium-halogen lamp is used as the light source. (Avalight-DH-S BAL), a grating spectrometer (Avaspec-ULS3648) is used as detector. The accessible spectral range of the system is between 200 and 1100 nm.

Two different types of photoluminescence measurements were performed within the scope of this work. In both cases the sample is excited with a laser and the fluorescence is detected spectrally. In the case of classical photoluminescence measurements, the complete spectrum was recorded. The different components in the spectrum provide information about optical transitions in the material under investigation, whose spectral intensity is a measure of the quantum yield of a semiconductor at a fixed layer thickness. The quantum yield was as well measured quantitatively by using an integrating sphere.

In contrast, when measuring the exciton lifetime, the sample is excited with a pulsed laser and the resulting photoluminescence is time-resolved and detected at a fixed wavelength. Based on the temporal decrease of the photoluminescence intensity, a statement can be made about the exciton lifetime in the corresponding material. In this thesis the time-correlated single photon counting technique (TCSPC) was used to investigate exciton dynamics. For the measurements, a setup by Edinburgh Instruments (LifeSpec II) at University of Bern was used. The measurements were conducted and elaborated by Nikolaos Droseros from Prof. N. Banerji´s group.

3.3.10 Transient Absorption Spectroscopy

In pump-probe spectroscopy, a first laser pulse called pump excites the sample at time delay zero ($D_t = 0$). A second laser pulse (the probe) crosses the perturbed sample and measures the effect of the pump. If the probe is in the visible range, it´s called transient absorption (TA), and the setup is schematized in **Figure 3.8a**. For time resolution, the probe is delayed with respect to the pump, so that the response of the system can be sampled at various time delays. The

81

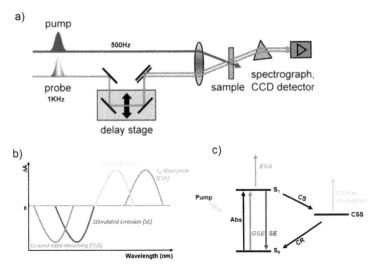

Figure 3.8: a) Transient absorption setup scheme block, b) Scheme of a TA spectrum with the different component evidenced and c) Jablonski diagram of the processes evidenced by the TA spectrum.

temporal delay between the two laser beams is achieved by varying the optical path-length of one of them, usually with a computer-controlled stepping-motor driven translation stage. In air (n = 1), an increase by 1 mm in the optical path corresponds to a temporal delay of 3.3 ps. Typically, delays from 20 fs to 2 ns can be achieved. For the probe, a white light continuum is obtained by focusing a weak part of the 800 nm laser output on sapphire. The probe beam is split in a signal and reference part and detected by two CCD cameras after dispersing the different colors in a prism or grating. Like this, the white light probe allows to measure the entire spectrum in the visible range.

In shot-to-shot detection, each transmitted probe pulse is detected separately. The detector is synchronized to the (1 kHz) repetition rate of the laser. On the other hand, the pump beam is chopped at half the amplifier frequency (0.5 kHz), meaning that only every second probe pulse experiences the pump in the sample. The TA ΔA^λ is therefore the difference between the absorbance of the sample when the chopper is closed and when it's open, according to Equation 3.6. The reference beam allows to correct for shot-to-shot fluctuations.

$$\Delta A^\lambda = log(\frac{I_{np}^\lambda I'^\lambda_{ref}}{I'^\lambda_p I^\lambda_{ref}}) \qquad (3.6)$$

Where I_{ref}^λ is the reference intensity, I_{np}^λ is the signal intensity after the sample when the chooper is closed (non-pumped shot) and I_p^λ is the signal intensity after the sample when the chopper is open (pumped shot).

Transient absorption can be measured as a function of wavelength or time. The TA curve along wavelength provides information regarding evolution/decay of various intermediate species involved in chemical reaction at different wavelengths. The transient absorption decay curve against time contains information regarding the number of decay processes involved at a given wavelength, how fast or slow the decay processes are. The processes that contribute to the TA signal (as schematized in **Figure 3.8 b-c**) are:

- Excitated State Absorption (ESA): Absorption of the singlet and triplet excited states that have been populated by the pump (positive TA signal).
- Photo Induced Absorption (PIA): If a reaction takes place in the excited state (e.g. electron transfer), the absorption of the products (e.g. charge separated states) appears in the TA spectrum as a positive signal.
- Stimulated emission (SE): Emission from the excited state that is provoked by the probe gives a negative ΔA signal at the spectral region of the fluorescence spectrum multiplied by λ^4.
- Ground state bleaching (GSB): The pump depletes the ground state population due to excitation. When the probe arrives, the absorbance of this population will be missing. A negative ΔA signal appears in the spectral region of the ground state absorption.

From the TA spectra, the dynamic constants of the processes of excitation or depletion of states can be calculated through global analysis, whose detailed procedure can be found in reference [92]. During this procedure, the entire TA datasets at all times after the pulse rise are simultaneously fitted to obtain the relaxation mechanisms and the respective time constants related to each process. Since an a priori kinetic model is missing, the data are simulated by a sum of exponential decays along with their amplitudes,

$$\Delta A = \sum_{i=1}^{2} A_i \cdot e^{-\frac{t}{\tau_i}} \qquad (3.7)$$

where A_i is the amplitude and τ_i is the corresponding time constant of each relaxation/recombination mechanism. A certain time constant is attributed to a relaxation amplitude that corresponds to the fraction of the TA signal that participates in this relaxation process over the whole detection range. Plotting the amplitudes vs. the probed wavelengths, the decay associated spectra (DAS) are obtained. DAS represent the amplitudes of the sum of the exponential functions that has been used for the global analysis procedure, extracted by keeping the τ as a constant. In the case of the TA spectra on OLED in device operating condition discussed in Section 4.4, a pulsed voltage was applied to the sample at the same frequency of the pump pulse (500 Hz). The measurements in this thesis were conducted and elaborated in the University of Bern by Nikolaos Droseros from Prof. N. Banerji's group. All measurements were performed with pulsed excitation generated by frequency-converting the fundamental beam of an amplified Ti:sapphire laser system (35 fs, 800 nm, 1 kHz, 6 mJ, Astrella Coherent) in an optical parametric amplifier (OPA, Opera Solo, Coherent). Subsequently they were chopped at half the laser frequency. The broadband white light probe pulses were generated by focusing the fundamental beam on a sapphire plate, then split into a reference and a signal component. The signal probe pulses transmitted through the sample and the reference probe pulses were spectrally dispersed in two home-build prism spectrographs, one for the visible and one for the n-IR, assembled by Entwicklungsbüro Stresing, Berlin and detected separately, shot-to-shot, by a pair of charge-coupled devices (CCD detectors, Hamamatsu S07030-0906). The probe pulses were temporally delayed relative to the excitation pulses via a micrometer translation stage, and pump-probe delays up to 2 ns were measured. The relative polarization of the probe and pump pulses was set to the magic angle, in order for polarization effects to be excluded. The pump and probe beams diameters were measured with a beam profilometer to be 1 mm and 280 µm, respectively, ensuring a uniform distribution of detected photo-excited species.

3.3.11 Contact Angle Measurement and Surface Free Energy Measurement

Surface energy is an important parameter in all printing processes as it provides information about the interaction of ink and substrate. It can be used to determine whether an ink wets a substrate, which is decisive for the printing result. For contact angle measurements, a drop of a liquid is applied to a substrate. Depending on the interaction between liquid and solid, a contact angle is formed between the substrate surface and the drop profile. The basis of the contact angle measurement is the Young's equation, which establishes a relationship between the surface energy of the substrate σ_S, the surface tension of the liquid σ_L, the interfacial tension σ_{SL} and the contact angle θ:

$$\sigma_S = \sigma_{SL} + \sigma_L \cos\theta \qquad (3.8)$$

The interactions between solids and liquids can be a manifold, but according to the theory of Owens, Wendt,

86

Rabel and Kaelble (OWRK) the total surface energy can be divided into polar and disperse fractions.[93] By measuring the contact angle of different reference fluids with known values of polar and disperse fractions of the liquid surface tensions, it is thus possible to obtain the polar and disperse fractions of the surface energy of the substrate by a linear fit function. In this work, the free surface energies (SFE) were determined via contact angle measurements with a KRÜSS DSA 100 drop shape analyzing system. Deionized water and diiodomethane droplets with a nominal volume of 0.75 mL were placed on the substrate. The contours of the drops and their contact angles, as well as the SFE calculations, were extracted with the help of the KRÜSS software.

3.4 Device Characterization

3.4.1 OLED characterization

In order to characterize the optoelectrical properties of an OLED, an external voltage is applied to the device and passed through, and the resulting current density and luminance (LIV characteristic curve) are measured. In this thesis a Botest LIV Functionality Test System was used. This consists of a SMU (Source-Measuring-Unit), a sample holder and a cover with integrated photodiode (**Figure 3.9**). The system is located in a so-called glove box, which is filled with nitrogen. All measurements are therefore carried out under an inert gas atmosphere. To measure the luminance, the cover with integrated photodiode is placed on top of the substrate holder. During the measurement, the photodiode

Figure 3.9: LIV measuring system from Botest consisting of sample cover with an integrated photodiode and sample holder with contacts.

is approximately perpendicular to the four pixels. Section 2.4 explained that luminance is a photometric quantity weighted by the sensitivity of the human eye in the emitted spectral range. Therefore, the system must be calibrated for the emitter material used. For this purpose, the emission spectrum of the OLED to be characterized is measured and a spectral correction factor is determined taking into account the spectral sensitivity of the photodiode. Furthermore, a geometric correction factor is determined using a calibrated spot luminance meter from Konika Minolta. This factor takes into account the geometric conditions such as the size of the pixels, their distance from the photodiode and the associated maximum aperture angle at which the emitted light is detected. The determined correction factors differ slightly for the four pixels because the photodiode is not exactly centered in the cover.

The SMU serves on the one hand as a voltage source and on the other hand contains the electronics for measuring the resulting current and luminance. The voltage applied by the SMU can be varied between -20 and 40V with a minimum increment of 1mV. The resolution of the current measurement depends on the size of the measuring range and lies between minimum ±20 nA and maximum ±20 µA. During the measurement, the SMU automatically adjusts the current range.

3.4.2 OPV characterization

Current density (J) measurements (J-V characteristics) are part of the standard measurement protocol for solar cells. Under illumination they reveal relevant parameters for solar cells, such as short circuit current density (J_{SC}), open circuit voltage (V_{OC}), fill factor (FF), and the device's efficiency (PCE), as explained in Section 2.5. The device is measured as well in the dark, in order to obtain the dark current density.

In **Figure 3.10** the measurement setup is schematized. After a 30 min lamp warming phase, the light source (LOT-Quantum Design 450-1000W Xe Arc Lamp Power Supply LSN555, Solar Simulator System LS0900 Series) can be calibrated with an inorganic silicon reference cell (ReRa Solution, covered with a KG 2 filter) to 1000W/m². The reference cell is connected to the source measurement unit (SMU, Keithley 2636 B). The light intensity is adjusted to the produced photocurrent of the reference cell by changing the

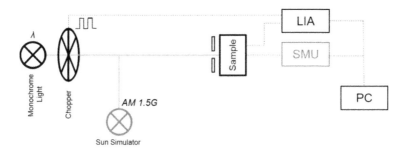

Figure 3.10: Simplified block scheme of the measurement setup for OPVs. In blue are evidenced the components necessary for the J-V characteristics (Sun Simulator and SMU). The other components are parts of the EQE measurement setup, where the lenses and the white light pulse trigger were omitted for simplification.

current at the lamp's power supply. Afterwards, the device is connected to the SMU via clips or a sample holder.

The EQE setup uses a xenon arc light source analogous to the sun simulator (450- 1000W), which is connected through an infrared filter and an additional high-pass filter wheel to a monochromator. Cut-off filters are used to avoid frequency doubling in the monochromatic beam. The entrance and outlet slits of the monochromator are adjusted to a reveal a ~ 10nm full-width-half-maximum (FWHM) wavelength distribution. An optical chopper with a 10-slot chopper blade suitable for frequencies from 20 to 1 kHz chops the steady light beam into the desired frequency (normally between 175 and 400 Hz) and passes the chopping frequency also as a trigger signal to the Lock-In-amplifier (LIA). A lens system collimates the monochromatic beam, which then passes an iris diaphragm placed in front of the device to ensure an illumination of solely the desired pixel. The device or the Si reference cell is connected to a shielded probe station mounted on an x-y-z translation stage, which again provides connections to the LIA and an SMU for applying a bias voltage. The EQE are then calculated from Equation 2.13, with a Labview software.

4 Properties of nanoparticle – polymer nanocomposites as interlayers

This chapter examines different examples of metal oxide nanoparticles:polymer nanocomposites as interlayers for solution-processed electronic devices.

In section 4.2, the bilayer PSBMA/ZnO is analyzed. In order to gain a better understanding of the functionality of PSBMA, Al/PSBMA and ZnO/PSBMA film properties are characterized. AFM images are used to assess the topography of the nanoparticle/polymer films and Kelvin Probe measurement, photoelectron spectroscopy measurements, IR and UV-Visible spectroscopy are used to characterize the properties of the ZnO/PSBMA interface. Section 4.3 deals with the properties of NiO$_x$:PEO blends, which were employed as hole transport/injection layer in OLEDs and OPVs. The topography of the layers has been studied with TEM and SEM in collaboration with Technion Israel Institute of Technology, the layers were studied as well through XPS and transient absorption spectroscopy. Finally, in Section 4.4 a well-known system, ZnO:PEI as EIL in OLEDs, is studied through Kelvin Probe, steady state and transient photoluminescence.

The PES results presented were obtained in collaboration with the Technical University Darmstadt. The IR spectroscopy results were obtained in collaboration with the University of Heidelberg. The TEM and the SEM analysis was performed during a research stay at the Technion Israel Institute of Technology. The transient absorption and the steady-state and transient photoluminescence

93

results were collected during a research stay at the University of Bern. Part of the NiO$_x$ samples was prepared during a research stay at the Imperial College London. Parts of this work have already been published in [94, 95].

4.1 Introduction

One of the most attractive features of solution-processable organic electronic materials is the possibility of using printing or coating technologies for the fabrication of optoelectronic components.[8, 11] These high-throughput technologies will allow the low-cost integration of devices such as OLEDs, OFETs, OPDs into flexible displays, wearables, internet-of-things sensors, etc. through a reduced energy consumption process.[35, 96, 97] A common challenge of these devices is to find materials that match the energy levels of the electrodes to the semiconductor in order to avoid energy losses and at the same time allow the sequential deposition of solution-processed layers.

In the field of organic electronics, increasing research attention has been dedicated to the investigation of novel interlayers that enable an optimal function of the electronic device, providing better charge injection or charge extraction, so that a reduced contact resistance and an improved alignment of the work functions between the electrode and the semiconductor are obtained.[15, 47, 98] A large effort is focused on substituting commonly used electron-injection layers based on low work-function (WF) alkaline earth metals or alkali metal halides. Recently, materials that reduce the charge injection/extraction energy barriers from the electrodes in order to obtain devices with lower operating voltages have been the focus of intense research. [13, 22, 47, 98] These materials need to be evaporated, have poor chemical stability in ambient conditions and are therefore not compatible with printing/coating techniques. [22] Conversely, anode interlayers are researched as an alternative to the commonly used PEDOT:PSS in order to obtain better electron-blocking property, a good pairing of energy levels with the HOMO of the active materials and better stability.[99]

A family of materials that have been deserving increasing interest for such purposes is the one of transition metal oxide nanoparticles, which can provide high-quality interlayers for both anode and cathode.[21, 23, 64, 99] Due to their air stability, optical transparency, and ease of synthesis, various transition metal oxides have been utilized extensively for interlayers in organic electronic devices. Hole extracting materials such as V_2O_5, MoO_3, WO_3 and NiO_x have been demonstrated to have the potential to replace PEDOT:PSS as an anode interlayer.[99, 100] Electron extracting semiconducting oxides such as TiO_x and ZnO serve as excellent cathode contacts for both conventional and inverted devices.[55] However, metal oxide nanoparticles often lack chemical stability, rendering them prone to exhibiting surface defect-induced resistances in organic electronic devices. Also, nanoparticles tend to aggregate; this phenomenon reduces their high surface area

95

to volume ratio and subsequently reduces effectiveness. By appropriately dispersing metal oxide nanoparticles into polymers, many of the shortcomings can be overcome without compromising the parent properties of the nanoparticles. Furthermore, the appropriate choice of the polymer host with specific functional groups may even lead to the enhancement of the properties of nanoparticles, as discussed in the following sections.

4.2 Poly(Sulfobetaine Methacrylate) and zinc oxide nanoparticles

4.2.1 Introduction

A promising approach to substitute low work function metals as Ca or Li, known to be highly reactive in air, is to use zinc oxide nanoparticles (ZnO). This material is vastly reported as electron transport/injection layer, with the advantages of being transparent and easily prepared and processed from solution.[21, 99] In the majority of the cases, ZnO serves as bottom cathode in the so-called inverted architecture device, where the ZnO is in contact with ITO and the active layer is deposited on top.[21, 100] In most of the published works, ZnO nanoparticles are formed through a sol-gel method, where a zinc salt is deposited from solution and converted in oxide *in situ* through calcination at temperatures ranging from 150 to 250°C.[22, 56] An alternative way of deposition of ZnO for low-temperature device fabrication is by using a ZnO nanoparticle dispersion as functional ink, which is commercially available and ready for use. However, processing ZnO from nanoparticle dispersions is known also for some technical difficulties: as nanoparticles, aggregates are frequent and the roughness of the layer can affect the device performance, as well as its big surface to bulk ratio, renders it prone to exhibit a strong effect of its surface trap states, hindering the charge transport and lowering the overall quality of the device.[56] A solution to this is to combine ZnO with a suitable solution-processable organic material. For this purpose, materials like self-assembled monolayers, Polyethyleneimine (PEI) and conjugated polyelectrolytes based on a polyfluorene backbone have been found to achieve control over the WF of an electrode and consequently device performance. [98, 101–105] In this context, conjugated polyelectrolytes are adaptable to multilayered device architectures, due to their solubility in polar solvents which are orthogonal to those used for subsequent layer deposition. Among them, zwitterionic polymers offer the advantage of being dipole-rich, while not containing any mobile ionic species which could negatively affect the stability of devices. The use of conjugated zwitterionic polymers based on sulfobetaine groups as EILs in OLEDs has recently been reported, showing WF reduction of up to 1 eV and improved device performance.[105–110] In this section, we report the use of poly(sulfobetaine methacrylate) (PSBMA): an air-stable, electronically neutral, solution-processable zwitterionic polymer, as cathode modifier in OLEDs. PSBMA has already been utilized in highly efficient inverted organic solar cells due to its strong dipole which rearranges on the metal electrode surface lowering its work function.[75] In this section, the bilayer PSBMA/ZnO is analyzed. In order to gain a better understanding of the functionality of PSBMA, Al/PSBMA and ZnO/PSBMA film properties are characterized, demonstrating that PSBMA not only reduces the WF of both Al and ZnO but additionally serves as a surface trap passivation for ZnO and improves its topography.

4.2.2   Film Properties Characterization

Bilayers of ZnO/PSBMA, SuperYellow/PSBMA, Al/PSBMA, ITO/PSBMA and Ag/PSBMA are studied through a comprehensive characterization performed by Atomic Force Microscopy (AFM), Kelvin Probe (KP), X-Ray and Ultraviolet Photoelectron Spectroscopy (XPS and UPS), Fourier Transform Infrared Reflection Absorption Spectroscopy (FT-IRRAS), in order to investigate its morphological and electronic properties. All the samples were fabricated by spin-coating. The thicknesses of the different PSBMA films were not determinable with accuracy by profilometry, by AFM or by ellipsometry, so in this section different PSBMA layers with different thicknesses are indicated by the concentration of the deposited solution at constant deposition parameters, ranging from 0.1 to 2 mg/ml.

4.2.2.1 Atomic Force Microscopy

It has been reported in the literature that the layer thickness of PSBMA films used to achieve a good performance in devices must be about 4 nm.[75] To determine the layer thickness of the produced PSBMA films different concentrations in 2,2,2-trifluoroethanol (TFE), from 0.1 mg/ml to 1 mg/ml, have been tested with constant rotational coating parameters.

In **Figure 4.1a**, the topography of ZnO and ZnO covered by PSBMA with various solid concentrations (0.5, 0.85, and 1 g/l) is shown. The initial roughness of the ZnO film is reduced by capping with the PSBMA layer with a *root mean square* roughness (RMS) from 6.7 to 3.3 nm, leading to a more favorable morphology for the subsequent deposition of the active material.

The optimum solid concentration of 0.85 mg/ml, that gave the best performances for the OLEDs and will be discussed in Chapter 5, presents an RMS value of 5.1 nm. There is no evidence of defects in the closeness of the PSBMA layer so that it can be assumed that a uniform, fully covering film is obtained.

As **Figure 4.1b** shows, the polymer emitter SuperYellow (SY) forms a very smooth film with low surface roughness. The optimal PSBMA concentration (0.25 mg/ml) deposited on top of SY, does not alter significantly the roughness of the resultant film (RMS from 0.7 to 1.1 nm), showing no disruption, meaning that PSBMA forms a uniform layer. However, at a concentration of 0.5 mg/ml, we observed the formation of drop-like clusters of PSBMA evenly distributed

99

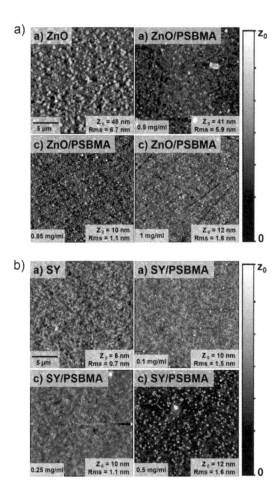

Figure 4.1: AFM images of PSBMA in various concentrations on top of a) ZnO and b) Super Yellow, the emitting polymer.

over the measured area which had a detrimental effect on the charge injection ability as suggested by the relative device performances, discussed in the corresponding section of Chapter 5.

4.2.2.2 Kelvin Probe

Kelvin Probe (KP) measurements were used to determine the work function of Al, ZnO, Ag and ITO films covered by PSBMA layers with various thicknesses, here defined by different concentrations. **Figure 4.2** shows that the work function of ZnO and Al settle around ~ 4 eV and ~ 3 eV, respectively, when the PSBMA concentration (i.e. thickness) is increased. For ZnO the biggest shift in the work function is obtained with 0.25 mg/ml (-294.5 meV) while for Al is 2 mg/ml (-206,3 meV). The work function shift for the optimal concentration regarding device performance are -278,6 meV (0.85 mg/ml) for ZnO, and -123,1 meV (0.25 mg/ml) for Al. The same measurement was then performed for PSBMA layers on top of evaporated silver and ITO. For Ag the biggest shift in the work function is obtained with 2 mg/ml (-380,3 meV) while for ITO is 0.5 mg/ml (-167,1 meV).

The decreasing work function trend with PSBMA thickness is in accordance with previous reports by A. Briseno and coworkers [75] and has been attributed to the formation of strong interface dipoles because of the polymers' zwitterionic side chain and its favorable orientation on the electrode surface. In Chapter 5 the device characteristics of OLEDs prepared with various PSBMA concentrations will be examined, evidencing the positive effect of the work function modification as reduction of the turn-on voltages

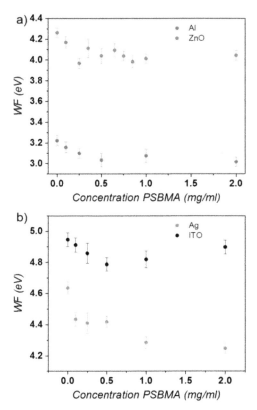

Figure 4.2: Work-function of aluminum and ZnO samples (a) and silver and ITO samples (b) covered with PSBMA layers of different thicknesses measured by Kelvin Probe.

of the devices. In the present case, the optimum PSBMA concentration for the best device performance (0.25 mg/ml and 0.85 mg/ml for regular and inverted architecture devices respectively) resulted from a trade-off between work function shift, suitable film morphology and minimized EIL resistivity, being PSBMA is an insulator.

4.2.2.3 Photoelectron Spectroscopy

The setup used for this section is in the *Clustertool* at InnovationLab and belongs to the working group of Prof. W. Jägermann at the Technical University of Darmstadt. Measurements were conducted by Florian Ullrich.

Photoelectron spectroscopy (PES) is an extremely surface-sensitive measurement method with an information depth of only a few nanometers. Because of this, PES measurements are very suitable for characterizing the interface between two materials. As a rule, the typical interface measurement is carried out in the following way: at the beginning, a pure layer of material 1 is measured. Material 2 is then thermally evaporated step by step onto material 1 and the sample is completely measured again after each evaporation step.

The electronic adaptation between the two materials can be derived from the development of the photoemission lines, in particular, the layer thickness dependent change of the line energies. For further details please refer to [46]. In this case, the aim was to measure the effects on two different substrates, Al and ZnO, of a thin layer of PSBMA, with processing parameters optimized through device performance studies. As schematized in **Figure 4.3(a-b)**, PSBMA was deposited on top of thermally evaporated Al with a concentration of 0.25 mg/ml, and on top of solution-processed ZnO with a concentration of 0.85 mg/ml.

Figure 4.3c shows the overview spectra of the different samples. With the deposition of PSBMA, the intensity of substrate emissions (Al or ZnO) decreases, as expected, as

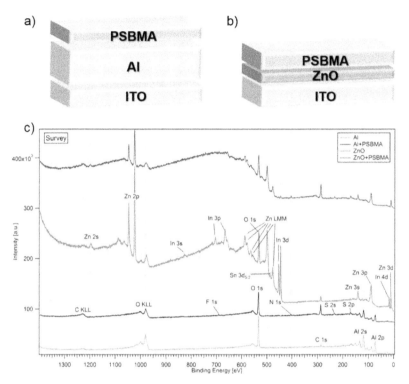

Figure 4.3: (a-b) Preparation of PSBMA films of different optimized layer thicknesses on silver substrates by varying the PSBMA solids concentration. (c) Overview XP spectra (survey). The higher the concentration of PSBMA, the higher the intensity of adsorbate emissions (N1s, C1s), and stronger the decrease of the substrate emissions (Al or ZnO). Since the samples were briefly in contact with ambient air during the transfer to the photoelectron spectrometer, small amounts of adsorbed carbon and oxygen are observed in the case of the aluminum, as well as residual carbon in the zinc reference. These measurements were obtained with the help of F. Ullrich, TU Darmstadt.

part of the corresponding photoelectrons are absorbed in

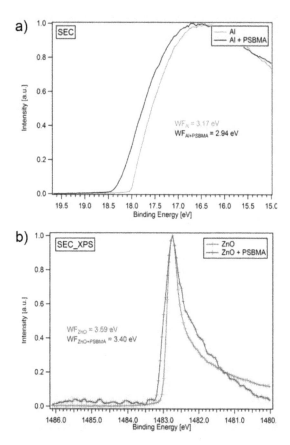

Figure 4.4: a) XPS and (b) UPS spectra of the secondary electron cutoff (SEC) region and the resulting values of the work function. These measurements were obtained with the help of F. Ullrich, TU Darmstadt.

the PSBMA adsorbate layer above. The intensity of the adsorbate emissions due to PSBMA (O1s, C1s, S2s, S2p) increases accordingly with the solid concentration. In the case of the aluminum reference, small amounts of adsorbed

105

carbon and oxygen are observed because the samples were briefly in contact with ambient air during transfer to the photoelectron spectrometer. Apart from these elements, no other emission lines are observed.

There is, therefore, no evidence of impurities in the samples. In order to determine the PSBMA induced change in the work function, the samples were characterized by UPS, in the case of Al substrates, and by XPS in the case of the ZnO to avoid UV-induced effects on the ZnO nanoparticles.[111] For PSBMA on Al (**Figure 4.4a**) we measure a decrease of the work-function by 0.23 eV from about 3.17 eV to a value of about 2.94 eV.

The native oxide layer on Al already induces a low work function, and thus the small observed work function reduction was expected and confirms what has already been reported.[75] Nevertheless, the work function of the samples examined here is still well above the typical values of Ca/Al cathodes, which typically have a discharge energy of approximately 2.7 eV.[46] For PSBMA on ZnO (Figure 1.4b) we measure a decrease of the work function by 0.19 eV from about 3.59 eV to a value of about 3.40 eV. A correlation between reduced work function and device performances can be done: the presence of the PSBMA induces lower operational voltages and higher current efficiency, as will be further discussed in Section 5.2. Moreover, these results are in good correlations with the KP measurements.

Al and ZnO samples covered by PSBMA were characterized by XPS in order to determine the nominal thickness of the

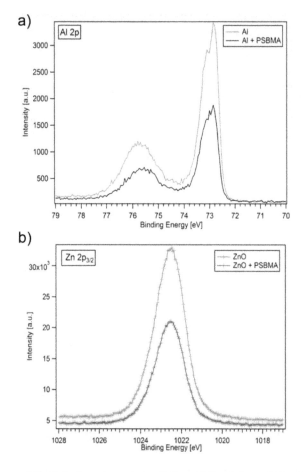

Figure 4.5: Relative damping of the Al 2p (a) and Zn 2p3/2 (a) emission lines through deposition of PSBMA films of different thicknesses. These measurements were obtained with the help of F. Ullrich, TU Darmstadt.

PSBMA films in case of the best performing concentrations in OLEDs (0.25 mg/ml for Al and 0.85 mg/ml for ZnO).

107

Figure 4.5 shows XPS measurements of the Al2p signal and the Zn2$p_{3/2}$ signal with and without PSBMA, respectively. As can be seen, the core level peaks of the substrates (Al and ZnO) are damped by the overlying polymer layer. This can be used to estimate the nominal thickness of the PSBMA layers according to Equation 3.5 under the assumption that a closed polymer layer is present.[46] The resulting thicknesses are 2.1 nm for 0.25 mg/ml of PSBMA on Al and 0.8 nm for 0.85 mg/ml on ZnO. The PSBMA layer on top of ZnO was expected to be thicker. However, due to the ZnO surface roughness (cf. AFM images in **Figure 4.1**), it is very likely that the PSBMA layer is not homogeneous/closed, in which case the calculated nominal thickness will be much smaller than the average thickness. Nonetheless, the 2.1 nm thickness measured on top of Al can be considered exact, and in good agreement with literature values [75] when correlated with the measured WF shift. The thicknesses of the different PSBMA films were not determinable in other ways with accuracy, neither by profilometry nor by AFM or by ellipsometry.

4.2.2.4 UV-visible optical spectroscopy

Figure 4.6 shows the absorption and emission spectra of ZnO, PSBMA and ZnO/PSBMA layers deposited from solution on top of quartz. The absorption onsets are at 375 ± 5 nm for ZnO containing samples, while pure PSBMA starts absorbing at 355 nm. All the absorption spectra recorded are modest in intensity, confirming that the layers are mostly transparent.

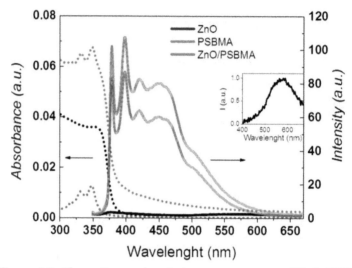

Figure 4.6: Absorption and emission measurement of ZnO, PSBMA and ZnO/PSBMA. In inset, a magnification of ZnO emission.

The emission of pristine ZnO is shown magnified in the inset, centered at 550 nm as reported in the literature.[111] The emission in the visible range of ZnO is due to the defect states of the nanocrystals, as already demonstrated in the literature.[111, 112] PSBMA shows a strong emission with resolved vibronic structure from 375 to 500 nm circa, with a broader shoulder that extends until 550 nm, which is two orders of magnitude more intense than the ZnO alone. The emission of the bilayer appears identical to the emission of PSBMA alone, concerning the peak distribution. The expected ZnO emission peak centered at 580-600 nm was not observed, although this may be because the peak is completely covered by the structure of the PSBMA emission. Due to the excessive difference in intensity, the absence of the peak typical of ZnO nanocrystal defects can't be used as evidence of emission quenching of the ZnO through the PSBMA through defect passivation. Nonetheless, evidence of such passivation have been collected through other techniques, as shown in Section 4.2.2.4 by FT-IRRAS and Section 5.2.2 through device characterization.

4.2.2.5 Infrared spectroscopy

Fourier Transform Infrared Reflection Absorption Spectroscopy (FT-IRRAS) measurements were conducted on ITO, ITO/ZnO, ITO/ZnO/PSBMA and ITO/PSBMA samples, with the help of Sabina Hillebrandt, from Prof. A. Pucci's group at the University of Heidelberg active in the *Clustertool* in InnovationLab. During the measurement of the OLEDs containing ZnO and PSBMA after the imposition of a pre-bias (will be discussed in detail in Section 5.2.2), it was observed the behavior of the devices suggesting the ability of the PSBMA layer to intervene on the trap states of nanoparticular ZnO with a passivation effect. This effect has been further investigated through FT-IRRAS, to verify the eventual presence of a chemical bonding between the ZnO nanoparticle and the PSBMA layer and to clarify the role of PSBMA in the observed passivation of the ZnO nanoparticles.

IR spectroscopy indicates that PSBMA replaces the adsorbates present on the pristine ZnO surface. As the adsorbates on the nanoparticulate ZnO mostly contain oxygen, the replacement may lead to a reduction of trap states at the interface. **Figure 4.7** shows the fingerprint

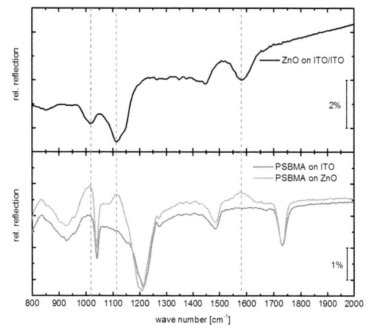

Figure 4.7: FT-IRRA spectra on ZnO/ITO (black) in comparison with PSBMA layers on ITO (gray) and ZnO/ITO (blue). The spectra in the lower graph are showing only the dielectric properties of the PSBMA layer. Measured with the help of S. Hillebrandt, University of Heidelberg.

region of the solution-processed nanoparticular ZnO on ITO. The adsorption bands at 1015, 1110, 1140, 1450 and 1580cm^{-1} can be attributed to C-O stretching modes of CO_2 adsorbed on the surface as well as residuals of the solvent (isopropanol).[113, 114]

The layer of ZnO nanoparticles itself does not show any characteristic vibrations in this energy range.[115] The IRRA spectra of PSBMA on ZnO or ITO in the lower part of the graph show very similar characteristic modes of PSBMA

111

independent of the substrate.[75] However, one can observe that the marked modes of the ZnO are in a very good agreement with positive features in the baseline of the PSBMA/ZnO spectra. This leads us to the conclusion that PSBMA has the potential to replace adsorbed oxygen-containing species as the intensity of these species is reduced with PSBMA deposition. The decrease of the adsorbates, therefore, may reduce trap states at the interface of ZnO and the subsequent layers.

4.3 Nickel oxide nanoparticles and polyethylene oxide

4.3.1 Introduction

Among anode interlayers, high work-function solution-processed transition metal oxides have become promising candidates to replace PEDOT:PSS as the anode buffer layer in organic photovoltaics due to their good environmental stability (being less acidic and less hygroscopic than the widely used polymer), high optical transparency and relatively facile synthesis. For this purpose, solution-processed non-stoichiometric nickel oxide (NiO_x), molybdenum oxide (MoO_3) and vanadium oxide (V_2O_5) have been employed as the anode interlayer to fabricate efficient OPVs.[23] In contrast to MoO_3, WO_3, and V_2O_5, the valence band of NiO_x is well aligned for hole transport with the highest occupied molecular orbital (HOMO) levels of many typical p-type conjugated polymers.[116] With small electron affinity (1.8– 2.1 eV), high work function (5.0–5.6

112

eV) and wide band gap (>3.0 eV), NiO_x is very promising hole transporting/electron blocking interfacial material.[117, 118] Recently, NiO_x layers, obtained through a sol-gel process from nickel organic salts precursors, have been successfully utilized in organic and perovskite photovoltaic devices, showing improved device performance and stability.[117–122] However, the used sol-gel process required a high-temperature treatment (250-400°C) to induce the decomposition of the precursor into a crystalline NiO_x nanoparticle layer followed by a plasma treatment which further oxidizes the nanoparticles. The latter treatment enhances the non-stoichiometry of mixed nickel oxidation states, and, in turn, the layer's conductivity.[75, 123] Such sol-gel systems can be printed using inkjet technology, leading to injection layers which display performances in various organic and dye-sensitized solar cells that are comparable to spin-coated systems.[124–126] In spite of these encouraging results, the high processing temperatures that are required to produce well-performing layers are not compatible with flexible plastic substrates and would be a drawback for the fabrication of cost-efficient devices by high-throughput printing or coating technologies.[38, 84] The system described in this section is based on a commercially available nanoparticle ink, which is a dispersion of already formed nanoparticles and therefore doesn't require a high temperatures post-treatment. In this section, high molecular weight polyethylene oxide (PEO) is used to help to disperse the NiO_x nanoparticles, hindering their aggregation after deposition without compromising film functionality in a solution process without the need of a high-temperature post-treatment.

4.3.2 Film properties characterization

Layers of NiO_x, PEO, and blends of NiO_x and PEO with the content of NiOx ranging from 10 to 99.9 %wt were fabricated through spin coating on different substrates and were characterized through Kelvin Probe, Transmission and Scanning Electron Microscopy, X-ray Photoelectron Spectroscopy and steady-state absorption spectroscopy. A layer of $P3HT:PC_{60}BM$ blend, a typical organic solar cell active material, was deposited on top of different content NiO_x;PEO blends and were characterized through transient absorption spectroscopy. Finally, contact angle and viscosity measurements were performed as preliminary tests in the ink formulation optimization for inkjet printing.

4.3.2.1 Kelvin Probe measurements

One of the main concerns that arise with blending NiO_x nanoparticles with an insulating polymer as PEO, is whether it affects the high work function typical of the NiO_x layer. The work functions of different content blends were measured through Kelvin Probe and are represented in **Figure 4.8**.

Increasing content of PEO brings the WF from 4.50 eV for the pristine NiO_x film to values close to 3.83 eV of the PEO alone. It has already been shown in literature that the treatment of the deposited NiO_x film with oxygen plasma for

114

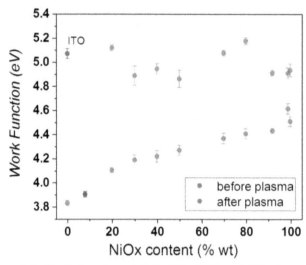

Figure 4.8: Work-function of PEO, NiOx:PEO and NiOx layers, before and after plasma treatment, measured by Kelvin Probe.

short times has remarkable effect on the work function and conductivity of the NiO_x nanoparticles, as it can be ascribed to a further oxidation of the NiO species operated by the plasma which allows the formation of the more conductive species NiOOH and causes a jump in the work function up to >0.5 eV.[127–129] Furthermore, it will be discussed in Section 6.2 that the lack of plasma treatment on the NiO_x as hole transport layer indeed heavily hinders the performance of the solar cell. The surface chemical composition of the NiO_x layer has already been reported to be affected by the plasma treatment, and it strongly influences the interfacial energy level alignment with organic active layers, and thereby the final photovoltaic performance of the devices. [118, 123, 128]

115

Through oxygen plasma treatment, the optimal work function (around 5.0 eV) is reached independently from the PEO content for the same plasma treatment. A bigger shift is observed for the blends, as in the case of NiO_x:PEO 40:60%wt where the shift is ΔWF = 0.73 eV. This suggests that the plasma treatment might serve a dual purpose: on one hand, it activates the optimal surface composition of the NiO_x nanoparticles, on the other etches away the PEO on the surface, exposing more the nanoparticles revealing itself as a necessary step for the optimization of the produced layers.

4.3.2.2 Topography

To clarify the role of the PEO in the quality of the morphology and the topography of the NiO_x:PEO blends, different layers were investigated with TEM, SEM, and SEM-EDS analysis. The images were taken with the help of Tanmoy Sarkar (for the TEM) and Artem Levitsky (SEM, SEM-EDS) from the group of Prof. G. Frey during a research stay in Technion Israel Institute of Technology. **Figure 4.9 (a-h)** shows TEM images of layers of NiO_x:PEO with 100%, 70%, 40%, and 30 %wt. NiO_x were acquired on thinner layers than the one later used in solar cells, as they were coming from a solution diluted in ethanol to avoid imaging disturbance, resulting in a total concentration of 1.25 %wt. of NiO_x. The nanoparticles appear as darker objects dispersed in a bright PEO matrix. From the inset in **Figure 4.9b** the lattice of a single NiO_x nanoparticle is recognizable. Image analysis enabled quantifying the interplanar spacings (d_{hkl}) averaging 0.24 nm which corresponds to the

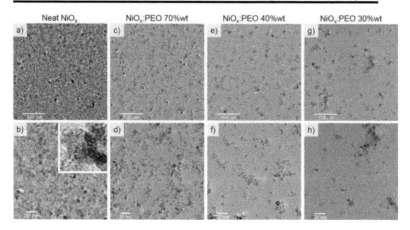

Figure 4.9: Low magnification (upper panels) and high-magnification (lower panels) TEM images of NiOₓ:PEO HTLs with different NiOₓ content. NiOₓ nanoparticles with diameters of 5-15 nm are observed. The inset (bottom, left panel) shows a close-up image of a single NiOₓ nanoparticle, the width of the image is 6 nm. The images were acquired with the help of T. Sarkar, Technion.

⟨111⟩ plane of the NiO structure.[130, 131] The cubic nanoparticles appear to be in line with previous observations.[132] The neat NiOₓ layer shows a mostly agglomerated morphology with several focal planes, which suggest the existence of multiple layers of nanoparticles.

The same consideration can be done for the blend 70:30 %wt., while both 40:60 %wt. and 30:70%wt show the appearance of a monolayer of nanoparticles. Blending with PEO causes a gradual dilution and a decrease of the agglomerate sizes of the nanoparticles from an average of ~ 55 nm to ~30 nm as observed in **Figure 4.9 (c-h)**, although some large agglomerates are still present in the blend with

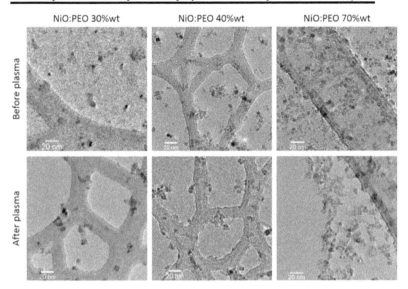

Figure 4.10: Figure 4.10 TEM images of NiOx:PEO blends with different NiOx content in proximity of the carbon grid before and after oxygen plasma treatment. The images were acquired with the help of T. Sarkar, Technion.

30%wt. NiO$_x$. The TEM images show that reducing NiO$_x$ content leads to a non-continuity of the HTL (on the nano-scale). At a NiO$_x$ concentration of 40%wt. the coverage is, however, sufficient to reduce the barrier for charge carrier extraction, effectively screening the effects of the bare areas. Additionally, the 40 %wt. blend seems to be the one with the closest ratio between dispersed single nanoparticle, agglomerates of few nanoparticles fused together, and amorphous polymer.

In **Figure 4.10** TEM images before and after plasma of the NiO$_x$:PEO blends were taken close to the carbon grid. As in the suspended spaces between the carbon grid the film is

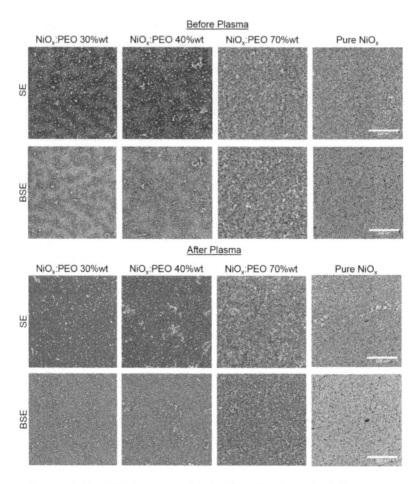

Figure 4.11: SEM images of NiOx:PEO blends with different NiOx content and pure NiOx before and after oxygen plasma treatment. Scale bar is 500 nm. The images were acquired with the help of A. Levitsky, Technion.

made only by the blend, it can be seen that after the plasma treatment the suspended part of the film is mostly

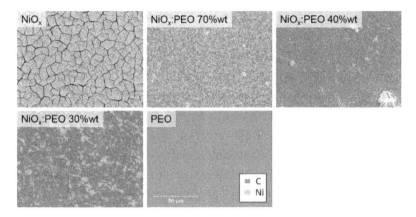

Figure 4.12: SEM images and EDS mapping of element C (in red) and Ni (in green) of thick NiO$_x$:PEO films with different NiO$_x$ content. The cracks on the NiO$_x$ film are due to the slow drying process to obtain the desired high thickness required to perform the EDS analysis. The scale bar corresponds to 50 μm. The images were acquired with the help of A. Levitsky, Technion.

destroyed for all blends, leaving a layer only on the surface of the carbon grid and confirming the etching effect of the plasma on PEO.

The surface morphology of the blends on a larger scale was investigated through SEM on films with the same characteristics as the one used in solar cells, although using silicon wafer as a substrate to avoid roughness-induced interferences. **Figure 4.11** contains the micrographs of layers of NiO$_x$:PEO with 100%, 70%, 40%, and 30%wt NiO$_x$, with both secondary electrons (SE) and Back Scattered Electron (BSE) detections, pristine and after plasma treatment. The SE images give information about the surface morphology of the film, while the BSE images give additional information on the chemical composition of the sample surface because the contrast depends on the atomic weight, so the Ni-rich zones are bright, and the C-rich zones are dark. The images before plasma show some separation in the SE as well as in the BSE images, suggesting that there is a phase separation of the materials in Ni-rich zones and C-rich zones. After the oxygen plasma treatment, such separation is not observable, confirming the etching effect of the plasma on the ITO and suggesting that a homogenous and closed layer was produced.   In every case, a homogenous and closed layer was produced, confirming that the layers produced for device fabrication have higher coverage than the ones fabricated for TEM measurement.

Element mapping by EDS on SEM images of pristine HTL is displayed in **Figure 4.12**. In this case, for instrumental accuracy, the samples were around 400 nm thick. Although considerably different from the ones used in the devices, this analysis can give a qualitative estimate of the elemental distribution in the layers. It can be observed that the continuity and the homogeneity of the NiO_x distribution are preserved for the blend layers with 70 and 40 %wt NiO_x, while HTLs with 30 %wt NiO_x shows a separation of domains comprised of NiO_x-rich islands, which is in agreement with what was observed for the TEM.

4.3.2.3 *Photoelectron Spectroscopy*

The effect of the plasma treatment on the blend layers was investigated as well through XPS. The O *1s*, C *1s* and Ni *2p* spectra for different NiO_x content layers, before and after

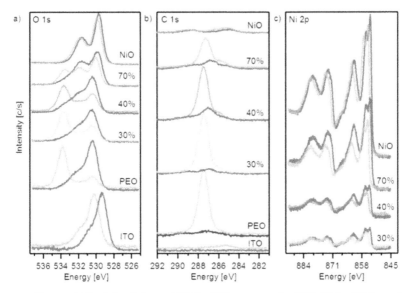

Figure 4.13: O 1s, C 1s and Ni 2p XPS spectra for ITO, NiO$_x$, PEO, and different NiO$_x$:PEO blends before and after oxygen plasma treatment. Blue trace is the corresponding XPS spectrum after plasma treatment. These measurements were obtained with the help of P. Reiser, TU Darmstadt.

plasma treatment are collected in **Figure 4.13**. Concerning the composition of the O *1s* and the Ni *2p* peaks in the NiO$_x$ before and after plasma, the nanoparticles are not as heavily affected in composition as reported in other works where the nanoparticles are formed from sol-gel deposition.[118, 123] It seems to be confirmed that the nanoparticles used in this work have a different stoichiometric composition compared to the ones used in works where the sol-gel process is used to fabricate them from precursors, and they don't rely as much on post-treatments (high temperatures or long oxygen plasma or UV-ozone treatment) to get the optimal mixed oxide composition. Observing the composition of the Ni *2p* and the O *1s* peaks, it seems that the amount of the different mixed oxides in the NiO_x nanoparticles are not changing through plasma treatment as the shape of the peaks is not modified. Interestingly, the Ni *2p* peak is observed to increase in intensity for the blends while remaining constant for the neat NiO_x layer. Simultaneously, the C *1s* and the O *1s* (534 eV) component of PEO are substantially reduced after plasma treatment. This can be explained by the PEO being etched away -at least partly- during the plasma treatment i.e. decapping the surface of the NiO_x NP component. The XPS characterization and the effect of the plasma treatment on device performances suggest that the main role of the PEO in the blends is to improve the arrangement of the NP in the film, acting as a sacrificial processing additive.

The etching of a polymer through the O_2 plasma is a known procedure, and this behavior of nanoparticles and polymers combination in UV-ozone treatment has already been observed to be very similar to our case with similar device performance improvements through surface etching by UV-ozone treatment of an interlayer composed of ZnO(NP):poly-vinylpyrrolidone for solar cells.[133]

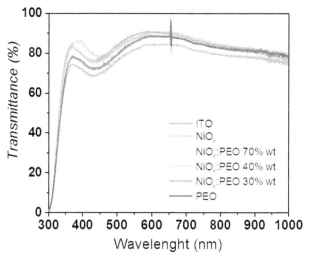

Figure 4.14 Transmission spectra of layers with different NiO_x content on glass/ITO substrates.

Table 4.1: Thicknesses of layers with different NiO_x content determined by ellipsometry, before and after oxygen plasma treatment.

	Before O_2 plasma		After O_2 plasma	
	Thickness (nm)	n	Thickness (nm)	n
NiO_x	17	1.7	14	1.7
NiO_x:PEO 70%wt.	10	1.4	8	1.9
NiO_x:PEO 40%wt.	9	1.4	3	1.8
NiO_x:PEO 30%wt.	11	1.3	4	1.8
PEO	8	1.4	0.5	1.2

4.3.2.4 Steady-state optical characterization

Figure 4.14 shows the transmission of neat NiO_x films and NiO_x:PEO layers prepared by spin coating from solution with different PEO content.

In all cases, the layers produced are very close to optical transparency. It can be appreciated that the transparency of the blend layers and neat NiO_x is comparable with the one of the reference substrate (glass/ITO), and therefore they don´t affect the active layer absorption. Interestingly, both PEO and NiO_x:PEO 30:70 %wt. decrease the transmittance of the ITO coated glass, from 78% to 74% and 71% at 400 nm, respectively. Confronting these results with the morphology study suggests that it´s due to a light scattering effect induced by increased roughness. The thicknesses of the layers and their refractive indexes n were collected by ellipsometry and are shown in **Table 4.1**. The thicknesses of the blends are lower than the film of nanoparticle alone, with a thickness of 17 nm for the nanoparticles and around 10 nm for the blends, while PEO is 8 nm thick. After plasma all values decrease, confirming the etching effected of the oxygen plasma on the PEO. For the best working NiO_x layer in devices, the thickness is ~4 nm. The measured thicknesses are in agreement with the optimal thickness reported in the literature for NiO_x layers, being around 10 nm.[121, 134]

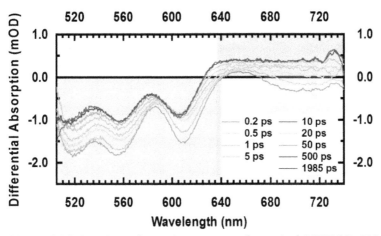

Figure 4.15 Transient absorption spectra of a typical P3HT:PC$_{60}$BM blend. The different coloured areas evidence the different optical signatures observed. Data collected and elaborated with the help of N. Droseros, University of Bern.

4.3.2.5 Transient Absorption spectra

Transient absorption measurements were conducted on P3HT:PC$_{60}$BM 1:0.9 blend films deposited on top of different NiO$_x$:PEO layers. The films were prepared with the same thickness as the ones used for solar cells. The aim was to verify whether different underlying layers of NiO$_x$, could affect the morphology of the active layer blend and therefore the device performance. The measurements were performed during a research stay in the University of Bern and elaborated with the help of Nikolaos Droseros, from Prof. N. Banerji's group.

An example of transient absorption spectra of the active material blend P3HT:PC$_{60}$BM is presented in **Figure 4.15**.

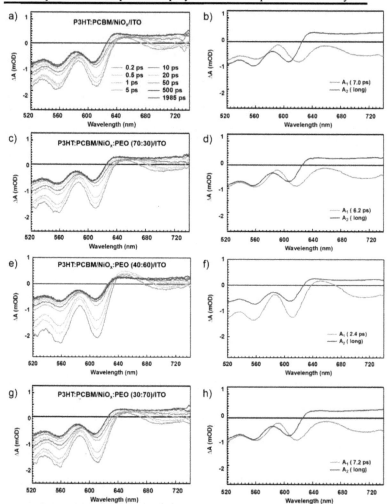

Figure 4.16: (a,c,e,g) Transient Absorption Spectra recorded at different time delays after excitation with 500 nm pulses and (b,d,f,h) DAS of the P3HT:PCBM blends deposited on substrates containing different NiOₓ:PEO ratios. Data collected and elaborated with the help of N. Droseros, University of Bern.

The area highlighted in red color, below 640 nm,

corresponds to the ground state bleaching (GSB) band of the P3HT. The GSB bans is observed due to the depletion of the ground state and the population of excited states. The area in green is the signal of stimulated emission (SE) from P3HT excitons, centered at 700 nm, which resembles the fluorescence spectrum of P3HT and is Stokes shifted relative to the bleaching signal. The area evidenced in blue, appearing at longer times, corresponds to the photo-induced absorption, where any absorption change is due to P3HT exciton dissociation by charge transfer to $PC_{60}BM$.

The transient absorption spectra for the bilayers of $P3HT:PC_{60}BM$ with different HTLs, after excitation with 500 nm, are depicted in **Figure 4.16** (a, c, e, g).

At early time delays (0.2 ps), the transient absorption spectra are dominated by the ground state bleaching of P3HT below 640 nm, and the stimulated emission of P3HT excitons centered at 700 nm.

At longer time delays (after about 10-20 ps), the SE is replaced by a flat positive band due to charge absorption and the GSB has a significantly reduced amplitude. In agreement with literature,[135–137] these spectral changes are due to P3HT exciton dissociation by charge transfer to PCBM. The unusual decrease of the GSB during charge transfer has previously been attributed to a different degree of delocalization of the P3HT excitons and charges.[135] We have quantified the time constant for the charge transfer by globally analyzing the dynamics at all probe wavelengths with an exponential function including an offset (as explained with more detail in Chapter 2). The

128

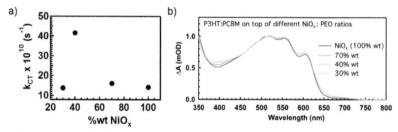

Figure 4.17: a) Charge transfer rate as a function of the %wt. of NiO_x content; b) steady state absorption spectra of P3HT:PCBM blends deposited on top of substrates containing different NiO_x:PEO ratios. The spectra are normalized at the 515 nm peak. Data collected and elaborated with the help of N. Droseros, University of Bern.

corresponding Decay Associated Spectra (DAS) are shown in **Figure 4.16** (b, d, f, h), with the fast component corresponding to the charge transfer and the offset corresponding to long-lived charges. Charge transfer is fastest (2.4 ps) for the 40 %wt. NiO_x:PEO HTL and slower (around 6-7 ps) for the other NiO_x:PEO ratios, as illustrated as well in **Figure 4.17a**. This points to a slightly modified morphology of the P3HT:$PC_{60}BM$ blend with the different HTLs, leading to different time scales for exciton diffusion through P3HT domains before they reach a PCBM interface for dissociation. Although the TA results point to the smallest P3HT domains for the optimal 40 %wt. NiO_x:PEO layer, the similar absorption spectra of all samples deposited on NiO_x:PEO indicates that the aggregation/crystallinity of P3HT remains comparable (**Figure 4.16b**). Moreover, the charge transfer in all samples is much faster than the exciton lifetime in neat P3HT films (about 400 ps),[137, 138] so that no significant difference in exciton recombination loss is expected, in

129

agreement with their similar short-circuit current. There is also no sign of charge recombination within the 1 ns experimental time window in any of the samples, showing the absence of fast geminate charge recombination (which would occur within a few nanoseconds).[136] We conclude that small morphological changes in P3HT:PCBM are induced by the different HTLs, but that they do not lead to significant differences in the charge generation efficiency that could explain the important changes in device efficiency.

4.3.2.6 *Contact angle and Surface Free Energy*

Contact angle measurements were performed to verify the effect of the presence of PEO and the effect of the treatment with oxygen plasma on the free surface energy of the films. The graph of the Surface Free Energy (SFE) before and after plasma treatment, along with the respective contact angles is presented in **Figure 4.18, Figure 4.19** and **Table 4.2**.

The wettability of ITO and NiO_x before and after oxygen plasma treatment are comparable. The total SFE changes for ITO and NiO_x from ~52 mN/m to 71.9 and 78.3 mN/m, respectively. Especially, the contact angle of H_2O undergoes a significant change from 61.45° and 59.24° before plasma to 9.39° and 32.61° after plasma, on ITO and NiO_x respectively. The contact angles of both H_2O and DIM on

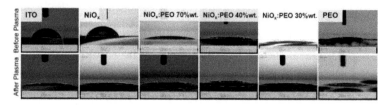

Figure 4.19: Droplets of water are deposited on different content NiO$_x$ films, showing different wettability for different NiO$_x$ content before and after plasma treatment.

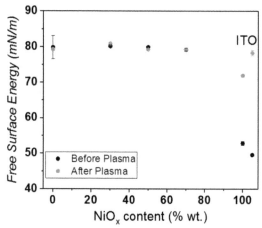

Figure 4.18: Free surface energy of layers with different NiO$_x$ content, before and after oxygen plasma treatment

PEO before the plasma treatment are very small (11.25° and 11.8°) which is related to the high SFE of pristine PEO. Thus, the subsequent plasma treatment does not alter the SFE significantly. Considering the etching effect of the oxygen plasma treatment, the SFE of the plasma treated ITO and PEO cannot be distinguished from each other. The predominant high SFE of PEO is also present in the blends.

Table 4.2: Contact Angle (CA) measurements for water and diiodomethane, of layers with different NiOₓ content, before and after oxygen plasma treatment.

	CA (°) before O₂ plasma		CA (°) after O₂ plasma	
	H₂0	DIM	H₂0	DIM
ITO	61.45 (±0.71)	35.09 (±0.37)	9.39 (±0.54)	26.02 (±1.53)
NiOₓ	59.24 (±0.81)	32.15 (±0.31)	32.61 (±0.32)	17.40 (±0.19)
NiOₓ:PEO 70%wt	12.88 (±0.70)	14.78 (±0.82)	7.43 (±0.36)	21.65 (±0.12)
NiOₓ:PEO 40%wt.	10.31 (±0.40)	12.79 (±0.60)	7.43 (±0.36)	21.65 (±0.12)
NiOₓ:PEO 30%wt.	8.41 (±0.17)	13.43 (±1.12)	6.67 (±0.17)	6.19 (±0.85)
PEO	11.25 (±0.67)	11.80 (±12.22)	7.43 (±0.36)	21.65 (±0.12)

Both, the contact angles of water and NiO_x are comparable to them of pure PEO, making the blends highly wettable even before the oxygen plasma treatment. The high SFE of the neat films and the blends after the plasma treatment is related to a good wettability for the subsequent solution processed active layer. It can be therefore concluded that the solution processing of P3HT:PCBM on top of the plasma-treated NiO_x as well as on the NiO_x:PEO blends should be favored by the high SFE of the underlying films.

4.4 Zinc Oxide nanoparticles and Polyethyleneimine

4.4.1 Introduction

Polyethyleneimine (PEI) belongs to the class of aliphatic amines, i.e. it has a non-conjugated backbone consisting of secondary and tertiary amines. The side chains of PEI contain primary as well as secondary and tertiary amino groups. PEI received great attention as a result of a publication in the journal Science in 2012.[18] In this publication, Zhou et al. showed that thin films of PEI applied to electrodes reduce the work function of a large number of electrode materials by >1 eV, in some cases by forming an interfacial dipole. Due to the non-conjugated polymer chain of PEI, very small film thicknesses of this material are usually used in devices. In the course of the last years, however, more university groups published papers on both polymers and discussed both the microscopic cause of the reduction of the work function and the application of PEI as EIL in OLEDs.[76, 139, 140] Kang et al. argued that the electrostatic interaction between the free electron pairs of the amino groups of PEI and the OH groups on the surface of metal oxides could lead to an alignment of the side chains of PEI.[141] With regard to the use of PEI as EIL in optoelectronic devices, it was stated in several publications that the layer thickness of the polymer films should not exceed approximately 10 nm.[16, 18, 139, 140] Recently, it has been proven that a blend of ZnO nanoparticles and PEI offers the advantages of both materials for electron transport and injection layers.[76, 82, 142] PEI lowers the work function of the ZnO nanoparticles,[18] mitigates the effect of the surface defects that result in trap states [112] (as already introduced as well for PSBMA in Section 4.2) while ZnO nanoparticles mitigate the tendency of PEI of accumulate holes at the EIL interface in devices deteriorating the device lifetime. This last interaction between ZnO and PEI was investigated by Sebastian Stolz from Dr. G. Hernandez-Sosa´s group in the Karlsruhe Institute of Technology and published as [82]. In this section, the aim is to give new insight on the mechanisms happening at the interface between the active material SuperYellow and the different EILs, observed in detail from device performance through pump-probe spectroscopy investigations. The effect of PEI on ZnO work function is investigated through Kelvin Probe. Then, the photoluminescence of SY is studied by steady-state photoluminescence and its photoinduced dynamics by time resolved photoluminescence. All the spectroscopic measurements were collected and elaborated during a research stay in the University of Fribourg with the help of Nikolaos Droseros from Prof. N. Banerji´s group.

4.4.2 Kelvin Probe

Figure 4.20 shows the work function of the different ZnO:PEI layers as a function of PEI percentage. The work functions of ZnO and ITO alone (4.11 eV and 4.74 eV respectively) were measured as references and they are in

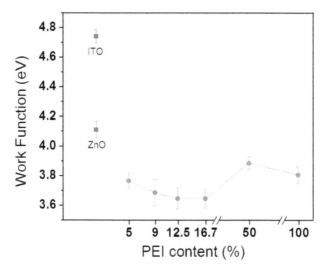

Figure 4.20: Work-function of ITO, ZnO and ZnO:PEI layers with different PEI content measured by Kelvin Probe.

good agreement with the values in literature (ZnO with 4.19 eV and for ITO is 4.8 eV [46]). There is as expected a clear relationship between the PEI percentage and the work function. At lower percentages of PEI, the work function decreases almost linearly until it reaches a maximum at 16.7 %wt of 3.64 eV. PEI. From there it starts to decrease until it reaches the value of 3.85eV at 100% PEI. Note that in the case of neat PEI, what is measured is the decrease of the work function of ITO (the substrate), which reaches a modification $\Delta\Phi = 0.89$ eV. At 16.7 %wt. PEI, the layer had a thickness of around 19 nm, and it was used as investigated layer for further characterization. The ZnO layer had a thickness of around 16 nm, and neat PEI had a thickness of

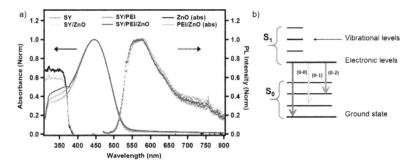

Figure 4.21 : a) Normalized absorption and photoluminescence spectra of a neat SY film and SY in contact with the different EIL materials. Data collected and elaborated with the help of N. Droseros, University of Bern. b) Transitions in the emission of SY, elaborated from [123].

around 2 nm, as reported as well in previous work by S. Stolz[82].

4.4.3 Steady-state absorption and photoluminescence spectroscopy

Figure 4.21a shows the normalized absorption and steady-state photoluminescence (PL) spectra of a neat SY film and SY in contact with the different EIL materials. The absorption spectra of ZnO and PEI:ZnO, in black and grey respectively, are shown in order to distinguish their contribution to the spectrum of SY. A significant contribution of absorption from ZnO is observed only below 400 nm. Based on the absorption spectra, an excitation wavelength of 430 nm for the time resolved photoluminescence measurements was chosen, while the

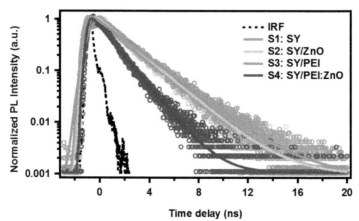

Figure 4.22: Emission decay of SY emission at 550 nm, with excitation at 430 nm, through TCSPC spectroscopy. Data collected and elaborated with the help of N. Droseros, University of Bern.

PL dynamics were collected at 550 nm. The emission is very broad covering a big part of the visible and extending into the near-infrared region. Its maximum covers the region between 550 nm and 590 nm, as the name SuperYellow suggests. The absorption of the substrate was subtracted, therefore the absorption spectra stop close to 300 nm. Based on the work of A. P. Monkman and coworkers [143], where the temperature dependence of the SY emission was studied, different wavelength regions in the PL spectrum can be attributed to the different transitions 0-0, 0-1 and 0-2 of the fluorescence (**Figure 4.21b**). The same diagram will be used in order to attribute the different signatures observed in the TA spectra that will be discussed in Chapter 5. In order to study the interaction between the SY and the

Table 4.3: PLQY, PLQY normalized to the highest value and PL lifetime τ_{PL} of a neat SY film and SY in contact with the different EIL materials. Data collected and elaborated with the help of N. Droseros, University of Bern.

	PLQY	PLQY (normalized)	τ_{PL} (ns)
SY	50 %	1	2.2
SY/ZnO	43 %	0.86	2.2
SY/PEI	50 %	1	2.4
SY/ZnO:PEI	25 %	0.5	1.5

different layers, the photoluminescence quantum yield (PLQY) was measured by using an integrating sphere. The results are collected in **Table 4.3**, and show that indeed both ZnO and ZnO:PEI quench the emission of SY, suggesting that electron injection takes place from the SY to the ZnO nanoparticle. Interestingly, the contact SY/PEI doesn´t show any sign of emission quenching. Correlating with previous electronic studies of the SY/PEI interface, these results seem to confirm that the electrons are indeed not transferred to the PEI, but tunnel through the thin PEI layer and are injected directly in the electrode. [50]

4.4.4   Transient Photoluminescence

Figure 4.22 shows the emission decay of a neat SY film and SY in contact with the different EIL materials. The extrapolated emission decay lifetimes τ_{PL} are collected in **Table 4.3**. The fluorescence lifetime decreases from 2.2 ns for neat SY to 1.5 ns for the ZnO:PEI, while it has little or no variations for both ZnO and PEI alone. The quenching of the PL emission, the decreased PLQY and the decreased PL lifetime in the case of the ZnO:PEI/SY indicate that, at the SY/ZnO:PEI interface without any electrode, upon excitation of the SY with 430 nm electron injection takes place from the SY towards the ZnO:PEI blend, confirming that the injection barrier is lower than the single components of the blend. In the next chapter, SY-based OLEDs are characterized by TA at 0 V and in forward bias, investigating the effect of the different EIL on the charge transfer dynamics.

4.5 Conclusions

In this chapter the electronic, optical and morphological properties of different examples of metal oxide nanoparticles:polymer nanocomposites are presented as interlayers for solution-processed electronic devices.

The first system investigated is the bilayer PSBMA/ZnO, as described in Section 4.2. AFM images showed that PSBMA mitigates the roughness of the ZnO nanoparticles and assessed an overall very smooth and even topography. Kelvin Probe measurement demonstrated that the WF of ZnO is reduced of up to 0.3 eV and the one of Al up to 0.2 eV by covering with PSBMA. Through photoelectron spectroscopy measurements the WF measurement was confirmed and the optimal thickness for PSBMA was assessed to be around 2 nm. FT-IRRAS spectroscopy demonstrated that PSBMA replaces the adsorbates present on a pristine ZnO surface, as the adsorbates on the nanoparticulate ZnO mostly contain oxygen, the replacement may lead to a reduction of trap states at the interface, as discussed more in detail in the next chapter. Finally, emission spectroscopy showed a change in the optical emission of the different layers, but due to the excessive difference in emission intensity, the quenching of the ZnO emission by the PSBMA through defect passivation was not determinable with certainty.

The second system examined is NiO_x:PEO blends, as described in Section 4.3. It was demonstrated that high molecular weight polyethylene oxide (PEO) can help to disperse the nanoparticles hindering their aggregation after deposition without compromising film functionality. Through Kelvin Probe, Contact Angle measurement, X-ray Photoelectron Spectroscopy, and Transmission Electron Microscopy it was assessed that the presence of PEO was beneficial for a better tunability of the NiO_x film thickness and morphology. Through SEM and TEM the nanoparticles appeared homogenously dispersed in the PEO, and thanks to XPS analysis it was observed that after the deposition the PEO gets etched by oxygen plasma treatment and thus acts as a removable passive matrix for the deposition of the NiO_x nanoparticles. The produced NiO_x:PEO blends, after the oxygen plasma treatment, showed the properties necessary for a good quality NiO_x thin layer, i.e. thickness close to the one of a single layer of nanoparticles and the appropriate WF of ~5 eV.

Finally, in Section 4.4 a well-known system, ZnO:PEI as EIL in OLEDs, is studied through Kelvin Probe, confirming that PEI lowers considerably the work function of the ZnO nanoparticles, and by steady-state and transient photoluminescence spectroscopy. The contact PEI/SY is not found to cause quenching of the SY emission, suggesting that no electron transfer process happens between SY and PEI. The quenching of the photoluminescence emission, the decreased photoluminescence quantum yield and the decreased photoluminescence lifetime in the case of the interface ZnO:PEI/SY indicate that upon excitation of the SY electron injection takes place from the SY towards the ZnO:PEI blend, confirming that the injection barrier for this interlayer is lower than the neat ZnO nanoparticles and therefore a better candidate for electron injection layers.

All the nanoparticle:polymer composite showed appropriate electronic and morphological properties to serve as interlayers, therefore in the next chapter all the mentioned nanoparticle:polymer nanocomposites will be applied in OLEDs based on the emitting polymer SuperYellow.

5 Application of Nanoparticle:Polymer Nanocomposites in OLEDs

In this chapter the nanocomposite systems analyzed in Chapter 4 are employed in OLEDs, as electron or hole injection layers. In Section 5.2, PSBMA is used as EIL in combination with ZnO nanoparticles for devices based on the commercial polymer SuperYellow. PSBMA improves the device performance which is evidenced by Luminance-Current-Voltage measurement and through characterization of electron-only devices. The role of PSBMA in inverted architecture devices as trap-filling, passivation layer on the ZnO is discussed in Section 5.2.1. In Section 5.2.2 the PSBMA/ZnO system is used in combination with another commercial polymer, F8BT, also improving the device performance. In Section 5.3, the system NiO_x:PEO is employed as HTL in SY based devices, giving only a modest improvement in the performance. In Section 5.4, reference devices with ZnO and ZnO:PEI is discussed and related to the internal process dynamics studied through ultrafast pump-probe spectroscopy. Parts of these results have been published in [95].

5.1 Introduction

The rapid development of organic electronics in recent decades has been the result of vast joint efforts in the scientific and engineering communities. OLED-displays are arguably the most established organic semiconductor

143

technology. Ultra-high-resolution OLED displays are now available in the consumer electronics market with high brightness, extreme contrast, rich color rendering and long operational lifetime.[10] Furthermore, major advances in OLED technology are expected in the field of high-performance lighting, where improvements are still needed in terms of color rendering index, high efficiency, high brightness, and durability. [11]

One of the most important directions of development lies in the field of interface engineering, as organic electronic devices are generally made up of several layers of different materials whose arrangement determines the final device architecture and the device performance. Solution processability is a feature that is highly requested for interlayer materials and researched as well for every layer component of the device.

The OLED layer stacks used for the devices examined in this chapter is shown in **Figure 5.1(a-b)**. The active layer, an electroluminescent polymer, is sandwiched between two charge injection materials (respectively for electron and holes) and it's enclosed between the two electrodes cathode and anode. Typically, when the hole injection layer and the cathode are the bottom electrode it is called a regular device architecture. Reversely, when the electron injection layer and the anode serve as the bottom contact it is called an inverted device architecture.

During the operation of the device, the electrons must pass through different interfaces in their paths. Interfaces often have a charge injection barrier that complicates electrons

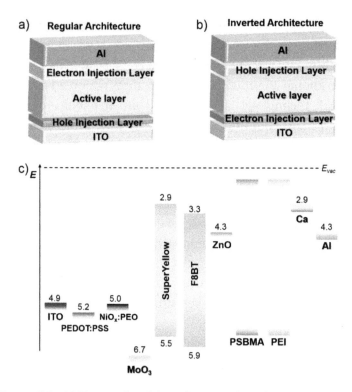

Figure 5.1: OLED regular (a) and inverted architecture (b) and energy levels (c) of the materials used. Due to the non-conjugated polymer chain, both PEI and PSBMA should be insulators. However, since the exact location of the energy levels is not known, the values were roughly approximated. In this diagram, any differences in vacuum energy between the materials and band deflections within the materials were not taken into account.

passing through, resulting in high operating voltages and low efficiency of organic electronic devices, reducing the lifetime of the device as well. One of the most important types of interface in an organic device is the interface between the electrode material and the organic semiconductor. These interfaces must allow charge carriers (electrons or holes) to pass easily across the material boundary with minimal resistance. Low-resistance electrode/organic interfaces are, however, not easy to achieve.

The need to solve this problem gave rise to the field of interface engineering in organic electronics.[13, 14] Interface engineering often involves tailoring the electron energy levels of the materials that are in contact with one another, in order to minimize or eliminate the charge-injection barrier.

In OLEDs, there are two types of charge injection contacts; electron-injecting and hole-injecting contacts. Low-resistance electron-injecting contacts require the conduction band of the electrode (the cathode) to be closely aligned with the LUMO level of the organic semiconductor. Conversely, low-resistance hole-injecting electrodes (the anode) require that the electrode's Fermi level is closely matched with the organic's HOMO level.

The OLEDs examined in this chapter were manufactured in accordance with what described in Chapter 2. PEDOT:PSS (Clevios PVPAI 4083), ZnO (Nanograde N10), NiO$_x$ (Nanograde P21), SuperYellow (SY), F8BT, PSBMA, and PEI were deposited by spin coating and the processing parameters are summarized in Table A.1. Aluminum was evaporated for the top electrode.

As shown by the energy levels of the materials used is shown in **Figure 5.1c**, there is a large energy difference between the LUMO of SY and the position of the Fermi energy in aluminum (Al = 4. 3 eV [46]), therefore rendering a EIL necessary for the efficient injection of electrons from the Al electrode into the SY layer. Due to its non-conjugated polymer chain, both PSBMA and PEI should be insulators. However, the exact position of the energy levels is not known and so are roughly approximated. Any differences in vacuum energy between and band edge bending within the materials are not taken into account.

Transition metal oxides are particularly versatile materials for use as buffer layers, as they can be used to achieve efficient charge injection for nearly any type of electrode. These materials can possess a wide range of work functions, spanning from extreme low of 3.5 eV for defective ZrO_2 to the extreme high of 7.0 eV for stoichiometric V_2O_5.[99]

The first reported use of oxide buffer layers in OLEDs was by Shizuori Tokito and coworkers in 1996.[19] Transition metal oxides are now components in many of the current record-breaking devices reported in the literature, including perovskites-based devices.[26, 27] Low work-function transition metal oxides, such as ZnO, are used as electron-injection buffer layers for cathodes. Reversely, high-work function metal oxides, such as MoO_3 and NiO_x are often used as hole-injecting buffer layers for anodes.

Transition metal oxides layers can be produced by solution processing by liquid deposition of a precursor followed by high-temperature calcination (sol-gel method), and by deposition of a nanoparticle dispersion in a low-temperature fabrication route. However, nanoparticles often present technical criticalities. Given the high surface/bulk ratio, they suffer more of surface-induced effects as trap/defect states, and they tend to agglomerate with a detrimental effect on the final morphology of the buffer layer. In order to mitigate these issues various kinds of polymers, from conjugated polyelectrolytes to insulators, can be employed to offer a hybrid solution.[32, 78]

5.2 PSBMA or ZnO/PSBMA as Electron Injection Layer in OLEDs

A promising approach to substitute low work function metals as Ca or Li, known to be highly reactive in air, is to use conjugated polyelectrolytes to offer a hybrid solution to these problems, as they are adaptable to multilayered device architectures, due to their solubility in polar solvents which are orthogonal to those used for subsequent layer deposition.

Zinc oxide nanoparticles (ZnO) are also vastly reported as electron transport/injection layer, with the advantages of being transparent and easily prepared and processed from solution.[22, 29] Nonetheless, ZnO nanoparticles have been as well vastly reported to present reduced efficiency as they lead to electron trapping and a high series resistance because of the presence of traps/defects with adsorbed oxygen on the nanoparticle surfaces. Conjugated polyelectrolytes or self-assembled monolayers can be used to address these issues. In this section, the use of poly(sulfobetaine methacrylate) (PSBMA) is reported: an

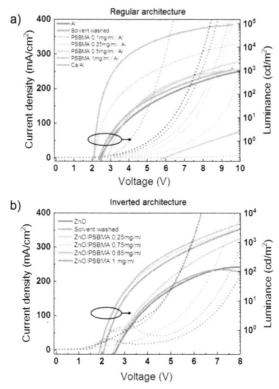

Figure 5.2: LIV-characteristics of devices with regular (a) and inverted (b) device architectures with selected PSBMA concentrations, compared to devices with no EIL.

air-stable, electronically neutral, solution-processable zwitterionic polymer, as cathode modifier in OLEDs. PSBMA has already been utilized in highly efficient inverted organic solar cells due to its strong dipole which rearranges on the metal electrode surface lowering its work function.[75] Here, we demonstrate that PSBMA not only enables lower operational voltages by reducing the

Table 5.1: Main device parameters for regular architecture devices for increasing concentration of PSBMA.

	Turn-On Voltage [V]	Max Current Efficiency [cd/A]	Max Luminous Efficacy [lm/W]
Bare Al	2.67 ± 1.01	0.11 ± 0.02	0.05 ± 0.01
Solvent washed	2.83 ± 0.11	0.19 ± 0.02	0.09 ± 0.01
0.1 mg/ml	2.91 ± 0.13	0.54 ± 0.14	0.2 ± 0.02
0.25 mg/ml	2.23 ± 0.03	4.22 ± 0.57	2.87 ± 0.01
0.5 mg/ml	2.87 ± 0.82	1.23 ± 0.07	0.62 ± 0.01
1 mg/ml	7.33 ± 1.70	0.04 ± 0.04	0.02 ± 0.02
Ca/Al	2.1 ± 0.05	10.7 ± 0.21	9.05 ± 0.33

Table 5.2: Main device parameters for inverted architecture devices for increasing concentration of PSBMA.

	Turn-On Voltage [V]	Max Current Efficiency [cd/A]	Max Luminous Efficacy [lm/W]
ZnO	2.93 ± 0.10	0.02 ± 0.03	0.01 ± 0.01
Solvent washed	2.83 ± 0.11	0.02 ± 0.01	0.01 ± 0.01
0.1 mg/ml	3.42 ± 0.43	0.18 ± 0.12	0.06 ± 0.02
0.25 mg/ml	2.57 ± 0.41	0.34 ± 0.12	0.16 ± 0.07
0.35 mg/ml	3.60 ± 0.44	0.07 ± 0.01	0.03 ± 0.01
0.5 mg/ml	2.15 ± 0.36	0.86 ± 0.19	0.47 ± 0.17
0.65 mg/ml	1.93 ± 0.07	1.12 ± 0.06	0.65 ± 0.07
0.75 mg/ml	2.18 ± 0.16	1.30 ± 0.09	0.68 ± 0.11
0.85 mg/ml	2.14 ± 0.08	1.46 ± 0.01	0.69 ± 0.08
1 mg/ml	2.25 ± 0.17	1.29 ± 0.09	0.64 ± 0.01

injection barriers of Al and ZnO but additionally serves as a surface trap passivation for ZnO rendering the device characteristics more stable under operation conditions. The most important criterion for assessing the quality of a

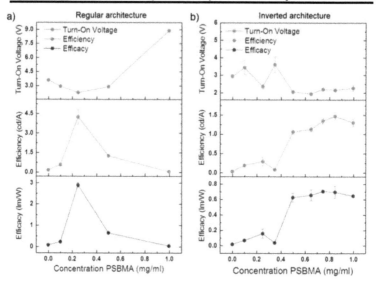

Figure 5.3: Trend of main device figures of merit as a function of PSBMA concentration: turn-on voltage, current efficiency and luminous efficacy for regular (a) and inverted (b) device architectures. Each data point in is the average of at least eight devices.

charge injection material is, naturally, the resulting device performance. After the microscopic functionality of PSBMA thin films was discussed in more detail in the previous chapter, this section examines solution-processed OLEDs that use PSBMA as an electron injection layer (EIL). As device structures both the regular OLED architecture, in which PSBMA is applied between the emitter and top electrode and the inverted OLED architecture, in which PSBMA is applied between the bottom electrode and the emitter, were chosen for this purpose. This has the advantage that the results obtained can be directly compared with reference OLEDs with an Al electrode for the

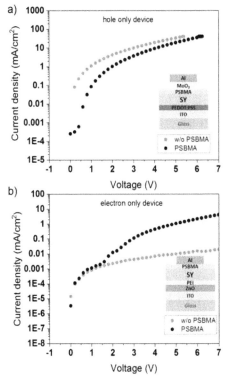

Figure 5.4: Unipolar devices with either Al or PSBMA/Al as cathode and MoO3 or PSBMA/MoO3 as anode.

regular architecture and ITO/ZnO electrode for the inverted architecture, so that the influence of PSBMA on the OLED performance is immediately apparent. Solution-processed OLEDs were prepared utilizing a PPV-derivative, commonly known as SuperYellow (SY), as the emissive layer. The PSBMA layers were fabricated by spin-coating with different thicknesses. Due to the small amount of deposited material, it was not possible to determine the PSBMA layer thickness with sufficient accuracy neither by profilometry, AFM or ellipsometry measurements. Therefore, in this chapter PSBMA concentration in solution is used as an indirect measure of layer thickness. **Figure 5.2** and **Figure 5.3** present the LIV-characteristics of the prepared devices as well as typical figures of merit as a function of PSBMA concentration (i.e. layer thickness). The values are also collected in **Tables 5.1** and **5.2** respectively.

For devices with a regular architecture (**Figure 5.2a** and **5.3a**), it can be observed that the presence of PSBMA increased the device performance for concentrations below 0.6 mg/ml compared to that of a pristine Al cathode. An optimal PSBMA concentration of 0.25 mg/ml results in a turn-on voltage (V_{on}, here defined as voltage at a luminance of 1 cd/m^2) of 2.23 V and a current efficiency of 4.2 cd/A, with a maximum luminance of $\sim10^4$ cd/m^2 at 10 V. The observed ten-fold improvement in luminance values compared to the pristine Al cathode is accompanied by a reduction of current density, suggesting more balanced hole- and electron currents. On the one hand, the reduced WF of PSBMA/Al (as commented in Section 4.2.2.2 and 4.2.2.3) should increase electron injection since it is observed to decrease operating voltages, however, the total current decreases. On the other hand, the hole injection is the same for both samples, leading to the conclusion that the reduction in total current comes from holes being blocked by the PSBMA layer thus increasing exciton formation probability and resulting in the observed luminance increase. The characterization of the unipolar devices for both charge carriers confirms that the presence of PSBMA in the device causes a lower hole current and three orders of magnitude higher electron current, respectively, as shows **Figure 5.4**. Compared to a device with Ca/Al cathode, the PSBMA/Al cathode injects a lower electron current, which being not balanced with the higher hole current injected by the PEDOT:PSS results in an overall lower device current, and therefore a lower efficiency.

In the case of devices with an inverted architecture (**Figure 5.2b** and **5.3b**), the best concentration of PSBMA was found to be 0.85 mg/ml. At this concentration, the OLEDs exhibit a V_{on} = 2.14 V and a maximum current efficiency of 1.46 cd/A. These values represent a reduction in operational voltages about ~ 0.9 V with a luminance almost two orders of magnitude higher than that of the devices with pristine ZnO as EIL.

This improvement is directly related to a higher current density enabled by the more efficient electron injection from the PSBMA/ZnO layer. It has been reported that solvent washing with pure solvents, especially alcohols, can positively affect the performance of organic electronic devices.[144] In order to rule out the possibility that the PSBMA carrying solvent (i.e. trifluoroethanol (TFE)) induces this effect, we fabricated solvent-washed devices in both regular and inverted architectures. Devices, where ZnO or SY were treated with pure TFE, exhibited comparable performances to the reference devices without any solvent treatment, as it can be observed in **Figure 5.2** and in **Tables 5.1** and **5.2**.

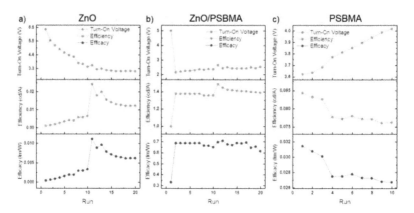

Figure 5.5 Effect of multiple voltage ramps on the main device parameters in inverted architecture devices for the three combinations used as cathode (ZnO, ZnO/PSBMA, and PSBMA only).

5.2.1 Effects of the PSBMA on the ZnO

ZnO nanoparticles are convenient solutions for electron injection layers, nonetheless, ZnO nanoparticles have been as well vastly reported to present reduced efficiency as they lead to electron trapping and a high series resistance because of the presence of traps/defects with adsorbed oxygen on the nanoparticle surfaces. In this section, the positive effect of PSBMA on mitigating ZnO defects is discussed. **Figure 5.5** shows the behavior of V_{on} after consecutive measurements using a voltage ramp of 0 to 10 V on devices with ZnO, PSBMA and PSBMA/ZnO as EIL. The other figures of merit of the device (current efficiency and luminous efficacy) follow the same trend as the V_{on}: for the minimum V_{on} the device present the highest efficiency and vice versa. The V_{on} of the PSBMA-only devices V_{on} steadily

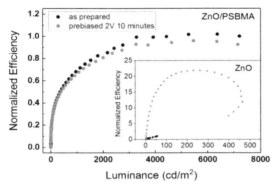

Figure 5.6: Effect of pre-biasing in inverted architecture devices as normalized current efficiency of the OLED plotted before and after the imposition of 2 V for 10 minutes.

increased until device failure after 10 runs, indicating a rapid degradation of the device. For ZnO-only devices, V_{on} decreases gradually until it reaches a stable value after ~ 11 runs, showing that the multiple voltage ramps have an activation effect on the cathode. This V_{on} reduction can be related to the gradual occupation of electron traps in ZnO[112] which usually originates from surface defects of the ZnO nanoparticles.[61, 111] Interestingly, devices with a ZnO/PSBMA EIL show a $\sim 60\%$ drop in V_{on} after the first voltage ramp and keep stable operation conditions until the twentieth measurement. Efficiency for ZnO-only device reaches a maximum around the 10th ramp and starts slowly degrading. The trend observed for the device's figures of merit suggests the ability of the PSBMA layer to passivate the surface trap states of the ZnO nanoparticle layer. These surface defects are sensitive to the presence of certain functional groups,[145] as a quaternary amine, carboxyl, or the sulfonate group present in PSBMA, and could thus be passivated by a capping layer of PSBMA. This effect is also evident in **Figure 5.6** where a pre-bias of 2 V was imposed for 10 min prior to the LIV measurement. The current efficiency of the device with pristine ZnO increased by 20 times adverting that the pre-bias helps to fill ZnO trap states and facilitates electron injection into the active layer. On the contrary, devices, where ZnO was capped with PSBMA, do not show a significant difference after the pre-bias demonstrating that the surface states responsible for the electron traps were passivated by PSBMA. In accordance with the conclusions of Section 4.2.2.4 from FT-IRRAS measurements, it can be inferred that PSBMA replaces the adsorbates present on a pristine ZnO surface. As the adsorbates on the nanoparticulate ZnO mostly contain oxygen, the replacement leads to a reduction of trap states at the interface.

The same electrical stress measurements were conducted on devices with a regular architecture, showing that such trap-passivation occurred at ZnO/PSBMA interface and PSBMA did not passivate the aluminum interface. **Figure 5.7** shows the variation in the normalized turn-on voltage (V_{on}) against the number of times that the voltage ramp (0 to 10V) is imposed. This measurement was conducted on Al-only, Al/PSBMA and Ca/Al devices, in order to distinguish the contribution of the EILs to the final performance. It can be noted that for PSBMA/Al devices the V_{on} increase for each ramp until the collapse of the device after 10 runs, indicating a rapid degradation of the device. For Al-only devices and for Ca/Al devices the V_{on} as a slight decrease

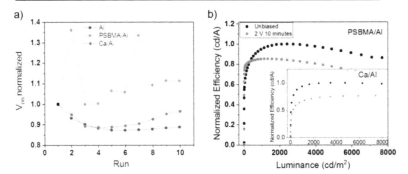

Figure 5.7: Effect of multiple voltage ramps and pre-biasing in normal architecture devices. a) is the normalized turn-on voltage for different runs of LIV voltage ramp (0 to 10V) on the same device; b) is normalized current efficiency of the OLED plotted before and after the imposition of 2 V for 10 minutes.

and start increasing again after the fifth ramp, indicating again that the device degrades before showing eventual bias induced improvements. As shown in **Figure 5.7b**, the pre-bias experiment confirms that for both Ca/Al and PSBMA/Al devices, the imposition of a pre-bias does not improve the performance, instead contributes to the device degradation. It can be concluded therefore that no effect of passivation is measured on the interface PSBMA/Al.

5.2.2 PSBMA or ZnO/PSBMA as Electron Injection Layer in F8BT based OLEDs

PSBMA was employed as well with the fluorene-derivative emitting polymer Poly(9,9-dioctylfluorene-alt-benzothiadiazole), commonly known as F8BT, in both

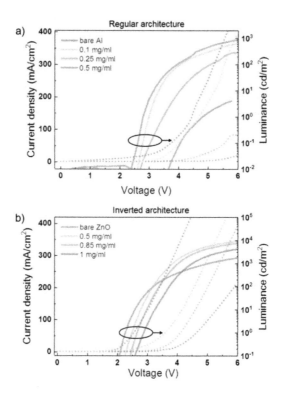

Figure 5.8: LIV-characteristics of devices with regular (a) and inverted (b) device architectures with optimal PSBMA concentrations, compared to devices with no EIL, for different thicknesses of PSBMA EIL.

regular and inverted architecture. **Figure 5.8** and **Table 5.3** summarize the performance of these devices. In all cases, the results were considerably modest compared to the performances usually reported for this polymer,[146] due probably to low quality in the material used for these

Table 5.3 and 5.4: Main device parameters for regular and inverted architecture devices for increasing concentration of PSBMA.

Regular architecture	Turn-On Voltage [V]	Max Current Efficiency [cd/A]	Max Luminous Efficacy [lm/W]
Al	4.77 ± 0.05	0.05 ± 0.02	0.03 ± 0.01
0.1 mg/ml	3.32± 0.72	0.15 ± 0.06	0.12 ± 0.05
0.25 mg/ml	3.50 ± 0.21	0.35 ± 0.06	0.22 ± 0.06
0.5 mg/ml	3.07 ± 0.53	0.19 ± 0.02	0.12 ± 0.03

Inverted architecture	Turn-On Voltage [V]	Max Current Efficiency [cd/A]	Max Luminous Efficacy [lm/W]
ZnO	2.22 ± 0.02	0.25 ± 0.01	0.11 ± 0.01
0.5 mg/ml	2.45 ± 0.02	1.87 ± 0.08	1.27 ± 0.08
0.85 mg/ml	2.75 ± 0.08	2.07 ± 0.3	1.45 ± 0.07
1 mg/ml	2.82 ± 0.07	2.22 ± 0.06	1.56 ± 0.03

experiments, which presented problems in solubility and consequently in film formation and emission.

For the regular architecture devices, PSBMA concentration of 0.25 mg/ml was the concentration that gave the best results, with a V_{on} of 3.50 V compared to 4.77 V of the bare Al, and maximum current efficiency of 0.35 cd/A versus 0.05 cd/A without EIL. For the inverted architecture devices, a PSBMA concentration of 0.85 mg/ml delivers V_{on} was slightly higher than the bare ZnO (2.75 V versus 2.22 V), but the current efficiency considerably increased from 0.25 cd/A to 2.07 cd/A. Overall, the quality of devices based on F8BT turned out to be inferior to the ones based on SuperYellow as an emitter. Nonetheless, also in this case, PSBMA improved the performances up to one order of magnitude improvement in the current efficiency for the inverted devices, confirming its reproducibility to more than one system.

5.3 NiO$_x$:PEO blends as Hole Injection Layers in OLEDs

A hole transporting layer (HTL) is usually required in a multilayer OLED to efficiently block electrons and excitons. PEDOT:PSS is the most common choice for this purpose, although great effort has been made in order to replace the PEDOT:PSS due to its modest chemical stability, high acidity and hygroscopicity. Despite the development of numerous small molecule organic hole transport materials, most of them are not compatible with solution processing because they can be dissolved or physically washed away by the solvents of the subsequent functional layer. Therefore, there are currently only a few reports on high-efficiency solution-processed OLEDs with a solution-processed HTL.[12, 16] Nonstoichiometric nickel oxide nanoparticles have already been demonstrated to be successful hole injection materials. In the case of OLEDs, several reports in the literature show that NiO$_x$ allows a more balanced hole injection, a higher hole current and overall a higher device performance. [147–149]

In this Section, the employment of NiO$_x$ and NiO$_x$:PEO layers in regular architecture SuperYellow based OLEDs is discussed. NiO$_x$ electrical properties have been studied in many works as a function of the temperature used to cure the NiO$_x$ thin film. This is necessary due to the nona)

b)

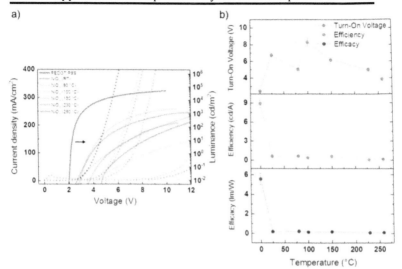

Figure 5.9: (a) LIV-characteristics of devices for different annealing temperatures of the NiOx HTL. (b) Trend of main device figures of merit as a function of the NiOx annealing temperature: turn-on voltage, current efficiency and luminous efficacy

stoichiometric nature of the NiO$_x$ oxide, and how the mixed oxide composition is created by heating the material in air. This correlation between composition and temperature of annealing has been evidenced in particular for the formation of the NiO$_x$ nanoparticles by calcination of an organic salt precursor. In **Figure 5.9** the LIV curves and the trend of the main device figures of merit are plotted for regular architecture devices containing NiO$_x$ as HTL, with a different annealing temperature of NiO$_x$. The layers used were roughly 40 - 50 nm thick in all cases and the films were annealed in air. This thickness is superior to the one recommended in the literature, which is usually lower than 20 nm.[99, 121]

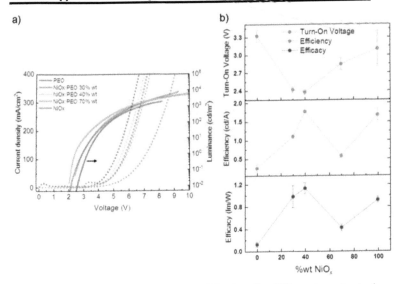

Figure 5.10: (a) LIV-characteristics of devices for different content of NiO_x in the NiO_x:PEO HTL. (b) Trend of main device figures of merit as a function of the NiO_x content: turn-on voltage, current efficiency and luminous efficacy

As the difference from PEDOT:PSS evidences an overall poor performance, it is interesting to notice for the nanoparticles used in this case, a lower temperature of 80°C is found to have a better performance than the >200°C recommended in many literature works. The best results were a turn-on voltage of 5.03 V, a current efficiency of 0.58 cd/A and luminous efficacy of 0.15 lm/W. Compared to PEDOT:PSS, the luminance emitted is neatly lower, as is also the current density. This is due most probably to the excessive thickness, and the consequent excessive resistivity of the NiO_x nanoparticle films, as already discussed in Section 4.3.

163

LIV curves and the trend of the main device figures of merit for devices containing NiO_x and NiOx:PEO layers as HTL, for different content of NiO_x are plotted in **Figure 5.10**. These layers were produced to be in the optimal thickness ($\sim$10 nm), annealed at 100°C and were treated with oxygen plasma for one minute before the deposition of the active layer. Extensive characterization of these blends is presented in Section 4.3. The employment of these same layers in solar cells will be discussed in Chapter 6. It can be noted that blending the NiO_x nanoparticles with PEO improves the quality of the devices in all cases, as they surpass both NiO_x and PEO used singularly. NiO_x devices have a better performance after the plasma treatment and with the reduced thickness, with an average turn-on voltage of 3.10 V, a current efficiency of 1.67 cd/A and luminous efficacy of 1.91 lm/W.

The best working NiO_x:PEO blend has a content ratio of 40:60 %wt. It can be assumed that this is the best working layer thanks to the considerations that have been drawn in Section 4.3 for the film properties, with the best compromise between film coverage, favorable work function, and conductivity. The performance of these devices goes up to an average turn-on voltage of 2.37 V, a current efficiency of 1.26 cd/A and luminous efficacy of 1. 12 lm/W. The sharp increase in all the figures of merit confirms that the best working HIL has an optimal thickness of around 10 nm, that it requires an oxygen plasma treatment and that its formation in the optimal morphology is facilitated by mixing the nanoparticle dispersion with PEO.

5.4 ZnO:PEI blend as Electron Injection Layer in OLEDs

As already mention above, Zinc oxide (ZnO) has been used as an EIL in inverted OLED devices as a result of its air-stability, high transparency, high electron affinity, and tunable electrical optical properties.[21] Conversely, organic polymers containing simple aliphatic amine groups, for example polyethyleneimine (PEI), have been employed as EILs to decrease the work function of ITO and lower the interfacial energy barrier for electron transport from the active layer to the electrode -approaching ohmic contact- by forming a thin interfacial dipole between the active layer and the ETL and consequently improving significantly the device efficiency.[18] As already described in Section 5.2, the application of ZnO nanoparticles (NPs) can lead to electron trapping and a high series resistance because of the presence of traps/defects with adsorbed oxygen on the NP surfaces.[61, 111] To overcome this obstacle, a double-layer structure employing a thin polymer layer can be adopted to decrease the work function of the metal oxide and further reduce the energy barrier for charge transport from the active layer to the ETL. When compared with devices based on a single metal oxide layer, the efficiencies of corresponding devices containing a metal oxide/PEI bilayer

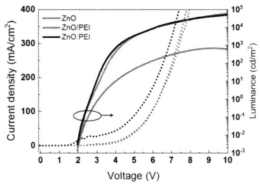

Figure 5.11: LIV-characteristics of inverted architecture devices with ZnO, ZnO/PEI (bilayer) or ZnO:PEI (blend) as bottom EIL.

Table 5.4: Main device parameters for inverted architecture devices with ZnO, ZnO/PEI or ZnO:PEI as bottom EIL.

	Turn-On Voltage [V]	Max Current Efficiency [cd/A]	Max Luminous Efficacy [lm/W]
ZnO	3.47 ± 0.61	0.09 ± 0.03	0.04 ± 0.01
ZnO/PEI	2.65 ± 0.07	8.66 ± 0.28	5.46 ± 0.45
ZnO:PEI	2.94 ± 0.12	8.78 ± 0.42	5.71 ± 0.61

as the ETL can be increased by approximately one order of magnitude. Combining both elements in one solution leads to the formation of the nanocomposite ZnO:PEI, which is as well an established system for electron injection for OLEDs and OPVs.[76, 142]

In order to elucidate the mechanisms occurring in the device and leading to the observed improved performance of the devices, this system was studied in this thesis by pump-probe spectroscopy under device operating conditions, giving for the first time insight on the mechanisms at the ZnO:PEI/SuperYellow interface during

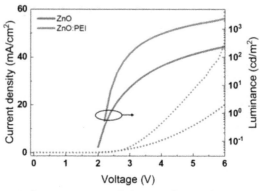

Figure 5.12 LIV-characteristics of the regular architecture devices with ZnO or ZnO:PEI top EIL. These devices are equivalent to the devices measured with transient absorption spectroscopy discussed in Section 4.4.

Table 5.5: Main device parameters of the regular architecture devices with ZnO or ZnO:PEI top EIL. These devices are equivalent to the devices measured with transient absorption spectroscopy discussed in Section 4.4.

	Turn-On Voltage [V]	Max Current Efficiency [cd/A]	Max Luminous Efficacy [lm/W]
ZnO	2.39 ± 0.04	1.21 ± 0.01	0.72 ± 0.06
ZnO:PEI	2.21 ± 0.01	5.59 ± 0.13	5.25 ± 0.28

the OLED function. The spectroscopy measurements were collected and elaborated during a research stay in the University of Bern with the help of Nikolaos Droseros, from Prof. N. Banerji's group.

For this characterization, different reference devices were fabricated for the comparison of the device performance with different EILs (ZnO and the ZnO:PEI blend) and as samples for the TA study. **Figure 5.11** and **Table 5.4** show the LIV curves and the main device figures of merit for inverted devices with ZnO, ZnO/PEI or ZnO:PEI blend as bottom EIL. The devices show overall state-of-the-art performances. ZnO without PEI shows a more resistive behavior, as evidenced before in Section 5.2. This blend has already proven to be very successful in literature, so it was expected that the use of ZnO:PEI composites as EILs would improve the SY-based OLED performance.[82] These devices, therefore, serve as a model, from which the analysis on the dynamics of the better injection properties through pump-probe transient absorption is elaborated.

In order to measure TA, the sample has to be partially transparent, so the devices where fabricated in an unconventional device architecture: ZnO and ZnO:PEI were used as top electrodes in a regular architecture (paired with PEDOT:PSS as HTL) instead of the more common inverted architecture (with MoO_3 and 100 nm Al) so the top Al electrode was only 10 nm thick. **Figure 5.12** and **Table 5.5** show the LIV curves and the figures of merit of the devices. Understandably, these devices have inferior performances compared to the reference devices shown in Figure 5.11. In particular, the current is an order of magnitude lower, most probably due to the reduced thickness of the top electrode. Consequently, the luminance is also considerably lower. However, the difference between the neat ZnO and the ZnO:PEI is still clear, confirming that PEI improves greatly the quality of the electron injection of ZnO nanoparticles also in these devices.

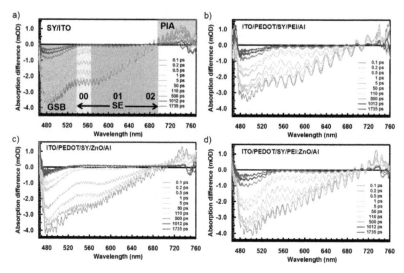

Figure 5.13: a) TA spectra recorded at various time delays following 450 nm excitation of (a) a SuperYellow thin layer on top of ITO. The different coloured areas evidence the different processes observed, (b-d) complete devices with ZnO, PEI and ZnO:PEI as EIL. Data collected and elaborated by N. Droseros, University of Bern.

5.4.1 Transient Absorption characterization

Transient absorption measurements were performed on SY film deposited on top of ITO and on SY based devices with different EILs. The aim was to verify how different EILs affect the device performance in terms of transient absorption dynamics of SY. The spectroscopy measurements were collected during a research stay in the University of Bern with the help of Nikolaos Droseros, from Prof. N. Banerji´s group.

An example of SY transient absorption spectra after excitation at 450 nm is presented in **Figure 5.13a**. The

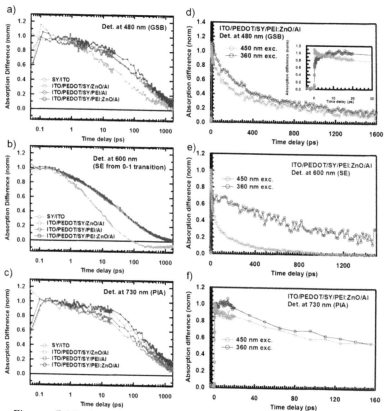

Figure 5.14: (a-c, left) Normalized TA dynamics recorded upon excitation at 450 nm and detected at the three different wavelengths 480, 600 and 730 nm corresponding to the GSB, SE and PIA, respectively, on OLEDs with different EILs. (d-f, right) Normalized TA dynamics recorded at the different spectral positions of GSB, SE and PIA upon excitation at 360 nm and 450 nm for the OLED with ZnO:PEI as EIL. Data collected and elaborated by N. Droseros, University of Bern.

oscillations present in the TA spectra are due to interference from the probe beam that is transmitted directly through the sample with the part of the probe beam that is back-reflected from the ITO, and are present in all the samples examined. The area highlighted in blue color, below 530 nm, corresponds to the ground state bleaching band of the SuperYellow, which is a negative signal because carriers have been excited by the pump and therefore are missing from the ground state. The area in green is the signal of stimulated emission, centered at around 600 nm, which resembles the fluorescence spectrum of SY (Section 4.4). The assignment of the emission peaks has been done according to the temperature-dependent measurements from [143]. The area evidenced in red corresponds to the photo-induced absorption, or the absorption from excitons, polarons or free carriers that have been generated by the pump and therefore can participate in transitions to higher states after absorbing the probe beam. The transient absorption spectra of the devices are depicted in **Figure 5.13b-d**. The spectra of the devices present the same optical features of the SY on ITO, and there were no obvious differences. Therefore, the TA dynamics were used in order to draw conclusions as shown in **Figure 5.14**. Upon photoexcitation, the GSB, SE and the PIA were already distinguishable in the first 100 fs. For these measurements, the PIA represents the population that is in the excited state, while the SE is the population that returns in the ground state. As can be observed in **Figure 5.14(a-c)**, the OLED with neat ZnO EIL had faster GSB and SE dynamics, showing that the excited state is depopulated rapidly. ZnO nanoparticles could be therefore quenching moieties for SY,

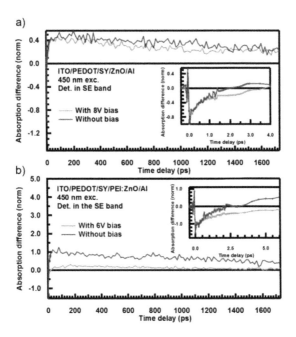

Figure 5.15: Normalized TA dynamics of the stimulated emission of SY in the OLED with ZnO or ZnO:PEI as EIL, at 0V or at positive bias (in operating device condition) upon excitation at 450 nm and magnified in inset, at delay times until 5 ps. Data collected and elaborated by N. Droseros, University of Bern.

as suggested as well from low PLQY that was observed and commented in Section 4.4. In contrast, this behavior was not observed when measuring the dynamics of the PIA at 730 nm, where the absorption from excitons, free carriers and/or polarons is probed. Both singlet and triplet excitons have been reported to form upon photo-excitation of SY.[150] Therefore, the origin of the population that remains in the excited state is not clear and needs to be further examined, although the lack of SE increase suggests that it is charges. Another set of measurements was executed by exciting the devices at 360 nm with the same carrier density as in the case of 450 nm, in order to see if more excitons would populate the electronic states of the SY due to injection of carriers from ZnO, which absorbs at 360 nm as can be seen in the absorption spectra presented in Section 4.4. The results for the case of the best performing device with the PEI:ZnO layer is presented in **Figure 5.14(d-f)**. As expected, the dynamics after 360 nm excitation showed a rise and were slower compared to the 450 nm excitation, because of the generation of the additional excitons that are created in the SY from the electrons that are injected from the ZnO. Combining these results, it can be inferred that ZnO:PEI is a better electron injection layer than ZnO, with dynamics closer to the ones of PEI, as ZnO seems to quench the exciton of SY.

The next step was to induce the injection of carriers into the SY electrically instead of exciting the ZnO optically, thus mimicking the behavior of an OLED under operational conditions. This type of measurement is inspired from the electro-modulated differential absorption spectroscopy, a technique that combines transient absorption spectroscopy with the application of a bias in OPV devices.[151, 152] In this case, since the devices studied are OLEDs, what is studied is the recombination dynamics of the charge carriers injected electrically in the SuperYellow vs. the excitons generated upon photoexcitation.

The devices examined were the OLEDs containing ZnO or ZnO:PEI as EIL. The dynamics extracted are collected in

Figure 5.15. It was observed that in both devices the forward bias caused the early time dynamics to be slower, compared to the dynamics in the absence of bias. The slower dynamics can be attributed to the efficient injection of carriers due to the applied forward bias that leads to the presence of more excitons in the system. The decrease in TA dynamics is more pronounced for the ZnO:PEI EIL than in the ZnO, confirming that blending with PEI improves the electron injection properties of the ZnO nanoparticles. However, at longer time delays the dynamics under applied bias are faster than without bias, signaling that additional processes, such as exciton-exciton annihilation at higher densities, are present. These results will be therefore further evaluated.

These measurements represent a first attempt of a new kind of OLED measurements aimed to investigate the charge injection and the exciton dynamics under operating conditions as a function of different EILs. In this first stage of evaluation we observed that, as also confirmed from the device performances, the presence of PEI in the ZnO:PEI blend used as EIL improves the electron injection abilities of ZnO nanoparticles, inducing slower dynamics of stimulated emissions in the SY that can be correlated with increased exciton population formed by charge injection and not quenched (as observed happening in the case of ZnO alone).

5.5 Conclusions

In this chapter, solution-processed OLEDs based on the PPV derivative SY and the fluorene derivative F8BT as active materials were fabricated to test the quality of different nanoparticle-polymer nanocomposites as charge injection layers.

In all cases, the use of these layers improved the performance of the device, compared to the bare electrode. For both the nanoparticle inks considered (ZnO and NiO$_x$), the use of the different polymers (PEO, PSBMA or PEI) resulted in the fabrication of nanocomposite interlayers that improved sensibly the final device quality and the stability.

The first system examined is ZnO/PSBMA bilayers as EIL for both SY and F8BT OLEDs. The maximum current efficiency of such OLEDs with a value of approx. 1.5 cd/A was clearly above the current efficiency of OLEDs with pure ZnO cathode, which was only about 0.1 cd/A. The characterization of the unipolar devices for both charge carriers confirms that the presence of PSBMA in the device causes a lower hole current and three orders of magnitude higher electron current, respectively. PSBMA not only reduces the WF of Al and ZnO, enabling lower operational voltages but also serves as a surface trap passivation for ZnO, stabilizing the device under operating conditions. This was evidenced by running multiple consecutive voltage bias ramps and applying a bias before measuring the luminance. The second system examined was NiO$_x$:PEO blends, employed as HIL in SY based OLEDs. It was demonstrated that the NiO_x film thickness must be as low as possible in order to reach the highest possible efficiency of the OLEDs. It was demonstrated as well that the film needs a modest temperature of annealing in order to obtain the best performance in the device. Lastly, blending NiO_x with PEO allows the formation of the best working HILs, with a maximum efficiency of 1.3 cd/A. The sharp increase in all the figures of merit confirms that the best working HIL has an optimal thickness of around 10 nm, that it requires an oxygen plasma treatment and that its formation is facilitated by mixing the nanoparticle dispersion with PEO. Finally, in Section 4.4, a novel characterization method is proposed, where a well-known system, ZnO:PEI as EIL in OLEDs, is studied through ultra-fast pump-probe spectroscopy, giving new insight on the mechanisms happening at the interfaces ZnO/SuperYellow and ZnO:PEI/SuperYellow in operating device condition. It was evidenced that neat ZnO has worse electron injection properties than ZnO:PEI and that the nanoparticles actually might be an emission quenching source for the SY. ZnO:PEI, on the other hand, induces slower dynamics of stimulated emissions in SY that can be correlated with increased exciton population formed by charge injection. The devices used for transient absorption spectroscopy were as well characterized with L-I-V measurement, confirming the high performance of ZnO:PEI as EIL with an efficiency of up to 8.78 cd/A.

In the next chapter, the system NiO_x:PEO will be studied in different types of solar cells as hole extraction layer, demonstrating the applicability of this functional nanocomposite to different kinds of devices.

6 Application of NiO$_x$:PEO nanocomposites in Organic Solar Cells

In this chapter the application of NiO$_x$ and NiO$_x$:PEO blends as hole transport material in different organic solar cells is discussed. In Section 6.2, the HTL is applied in standard P3HT:PC$_{60}$BM solar cells, showing a trend in efficiency dependent on NiO$_x$ content in the NiO$_x$:PEO blend and improving the device performance, demonstrated by J-V characteristics, EQE measurements and through characterization of hole-only devices. In Section 6.2.1, the NiO$_x$:PEO layers are produced by inkjet printing and integrated in the solar cell, showing the highest performance for these solar cells and obtaining at low temperature the same results obtained in literature with harsher post-treatments. In Section 6.3, the HTLs are applied in solar cells with more recently developed active layers, namely the low-bandgap PTB7:PC$_{70}$BM and the non-fullerene acceptor P3HT:o-IDTBR, although demonstrating only a minor performance improvement. Finally, in Section 6.4, NiO$_x$:PEO blends are fabricated with low molecular weight PEO and employed in the reference solar cells with P3HT:PC$_{60}$BM, evidencing that the high molecular weight PEO used before is actually a more dispersing agent for the nanoparticles. Parts of these results have been published in [94].

6.1 Introduction

Over the past couple of decades, organic and more specifically polymeric solar cells (OPVs) have generated

179

a)

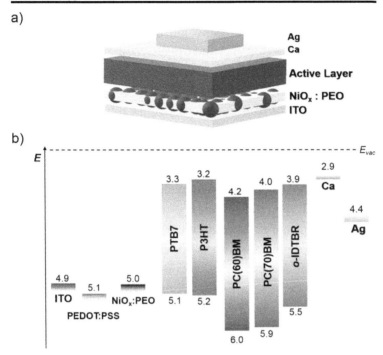

b)

Figure 6.1: OPV regular architecture (a) and energy levels of the materials used (b). In this diagram, any differences in vacuum energy between the materials and band deflections within the materials were not considered.

great research interest because of their potential as cost-effective devices for energy harvesting. [153]

Most OPVs are manufactured with bulk heterojunctions (BHJ),[154] in which electron-donor polymer and electron-acceptor fullerene derivatives are intermixed in nanosized networks that allow efficient dissociation and transport of excitons. A band-gap engineering approach for photoactive polymers allows the production of many low-lying HOMO polymers and tunable band gaps, resulting in improved short-circuit current (J_{sc}) and open circuit voltage (V_{oc}), two key parameters of photovoltaic devices. Device architecture optimization and the development of novel photoactive materials are the traction forces for research in OPVs, which have already demonstrated PCEs up to 15.6%.[7] Efficiency in a solar cell is a product of V_{oc}, J_{sc}, and FF. V_{oc} is determined by energy level alignment between the polymer donor and the fullerene acceptor and as well by recombination; J_{sc} is determined by the efficiency of light collection and efficiency of charge separation under large extraction fields, while FF is determined by the device series resistance, the dark current and the charge recombination/extraction rate under low extraction fields. **Figure 1a** shows the device stack scheme for the OPV devices discussed in this chapter. **Figure 1b** shows the energy values of the HOMO and the LUMO of the photovoltaic donor polymers and the acceptor derivatives of fullerene employed, as well as the work function of the utilized interlayers. The OPVs were manufactured in accordance with Chapter 3. The different layers were deposited by spin coating or by inkjet printing and the processing parameters are summarized in Table A.1. The silver electrode was thermally evaporated in high vacuum at a rate of 2 Å/s.

Unlike inorganic solar cells, where ohmic contacts can be made by surface doping, OPVs require alternative strategies for interface design. In particular, poor ohmic contact with transparent conductive oxides (e.g. ITO) or metal electrodes is due to inadequate matching of work functions, presence of interface dipole and high density of trap states.[12, 13, 47] To ensure good ohmic contacts between the BHJ layer and the electrodes, several interlayers have been used to extract the charges.[12, 15] Among the electrode interlayer materials used in high-efficiency OPVs, transition metal oxides are promising due to their increased environmental stability, greater optical transparency and simpler synthesis pathways compared to alkaline metal compounds (Ca, LiF), conductive aqueous PEDOT:PSS and other conjugated polyelectrolytes.[21, 99] Solution-processed non-stoichiometric nickel oxide (NiO$_x$), molybdenum oxide (MoO$_3$) and vanadium oxide (V$_2$O$_5$) have been employed as the anode interlayer to fabricate efficient OPVs. With small electron affinity (1.8–2.1 eV), high work function (5.0–5.6 eV) and wide band gap (>3.0 eV), NiO$_x$ is a very promising hole transporting/electron blocking interfacial material.[11,12] In contrast to MoO$_3$, WO$_3$, and V$_2$O$_5$, the valence band of NiO$_x$ is well aligned for hole transport with the highest occupied molecular orbital (HOMO) levels of many typical p-type conjugated polymers.[116]

The p-type semiconductive properties of these transition metal oxides are usually due to their inherent lattice defects, such as atomic vacancies. The metal oxides form ohmic contacts to the BHJ through favorable energy level bending at the polymer–electrode interfaces. In addition, the use of the interlayers prevents the direct contact between the BHJ and the electrodes where high densities of carrier traps or unfavorable interface dipoles hinder an efficient charge collection. Furthermore, ohmic contacts are important in order to maximize the V_{oc}, as the reduction of the built-in potential leads to an increase in the dark current as well as detrimental carrier recombination.

Recently NiO_x layers, obtained through a sol-gel process from nickel organic salts precursors, have been successfully utilized in organic (OPV) and perovskite photovoltaic devices, showing improved device performance and stability.[117–119]

NiO_x nanocrystalline layers are usually synthesized in sol-gel processes from precursor nickel organic salts which are then oxidized by bringing the deposited film to high temperatures, namely 250-400°C. However, the used sol-gel process requires a high-temperature treatment to induce the decomposition of the precursor into a crystalline NiO_x nanoparticle layer followed by a plasma treatment which further oxidizes the nanoparticles. The latter treatment enhances the non-stoichiometry of mixed nickel oxidation states, and, in turn, the layer's conductivity.[123] Such sol-gel systems can be printed using inkjet, leading to injection layers which display performances in various organic and dye-sensitized solar cells that are comparable to spin-coated systems.[124–126] In spite of these encouraging results, the high processing temperatures that are required to produce well-performing layers are not compatible with flexible plastic substrates and would be a drawback for the fabrication of cost-efficient devices by high-throughput printing or coating technologies.[83, 84]

This chapter is focused on the use of a commercially available nanoparticle dispersion ink of NiO_x for the fabrication of hole transport layer (HTL) in organic solar cells. The fabrication of highly efficient NiO_x thin films from this ink is challenging due to the low viscosity and fast evaporation of the solvent employed (ethanol). In order to overcome this technical difficulty, high molecular weight polyethylene oxide (PEO) was employed to disperse the nanoparticles, hindering their aggregation after deposition without compromising film functionality. This favorable film formation is observed to be beneficial when the NiO_x:PEO blends are applied as a hole extraction layer on OPV devices, improving device performance. Blending the nanoparticle ink with the polymer allowed the inkjet-printing of an efficient NiO_x layer without requiring high-temperature post-treatment, which was presented for the first time.

6.2 NiO_x:PEO in P3HT:PC_{60}BM solar cells

Organic solar cells based on the standard bulk-heterojunction P3HT:PC_{60}BM in regular architecture were fabricated to verify the suitability of the NiO_x:PEO blend as hole transport/extraction layer. The blends fabricated ranged through a weight percentage of NiO_x nanoparticles from 10% to 99.9% wt and confronted with films of neat NiO_x, neat PEO, and PEDOT:PSS. The NiO_x:PEO HTL thicknesses ranged between 4 and 8 nm and exhibited high optical transparency (> 85 %) in the visible range (as commented more in detail in Section 4.3.2.5). The measured thicknesses are in agreement with the nominal thicknesses (~10 nm) reported in the literature for NiO_x HTLs used in

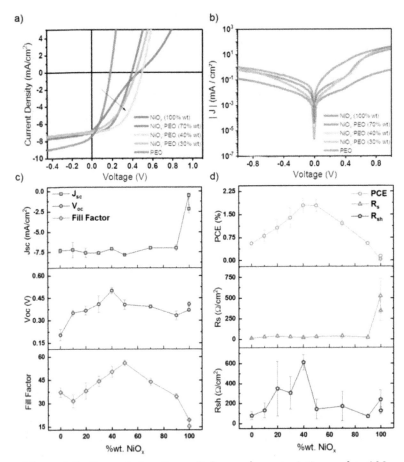

Figure 6.2: Current density vs Voltage characteristics under 100 mW/cm² (a) and in dark condition (b); deduced Jsc, Voc and Fill Factor (c); deduced PCE, Rs and Rsh (d) of solar cells as a function of NiOx concetration used to spin-coat the HTL. Curves and data points represent averages of at least eight devices.

OPV devices.[117, 121] **Figure 6.2** shows the JV-characteristics in dark and under 100 mW/cm^2 illumination condition of spin cast P3HT:PC$_{60}$BM bulk-heterojunction solar cells and their corresponding figures of merit as a function of NiO$_x$:PEO ratio in the HTL. It can be easily deduced that devices with either neat NiO$_x$ or PEO HTLs showed lower performances than any of the devices with HTLs composed of NiO$_x$:PEO blends. It can be observed that the neat NiO$_x$ was characterized by a distinct s-shape, with substantial losses in terms of J$_{sc}$ and FF when compared to the best working device.

This could be attributed to an imbalance in the different charge carrier extraction in the device: while the Ca electrode for electrons is very efficient, the pure NiO$_x$ or blended with a very small amount of polymer seems not able to extract charges as efficiently as Ca, with consequent accumulation of holes and inducing an s-shaped JV characteristic.[155, 156] The devices with PEO without NiO$_x$ showed a strong reduction in the V$_{oc}$, while the J$_{sc}$ doesn't differ much from better performing devices. As observed in Section 4.3.2.1 PEO has a WF sensitively lower than NiO$_x$, and while the layer is thin enough not to disrupt the conductivity of ITO, its presence is enough to cause an energy level mismatch responsible of the loss in V$_{oc}$.

Concerning the NiO$_x$:PEO blends, while the short-circuit current (J$_{sc}$) is not affected by the HTL, the power conversion efficiency (PCE), fill factor (FF), and open-circuit voltage (V$_{oc}$) show a bell-shaped dependency with PEO content. The best overall performance was measured at a NiO$_x$:PEO ratio of 40:60 %wt. Compared to the neat NiO$_x$

186

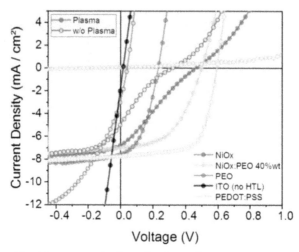

Figure 6.3: I-V curves of selected solar cells (spin coated) with bare ITO, PEDOT:PSS or different NiOx concentration, with or without oxygen plasma treatment before the active layer deposition.

layers, in the NiO_x:PEO blends the presence of PEO seems to be necessary for better photovoltaic performance.

To assess the reason for the bell-shaped efficiency dependency with HTL composition, we extracted the shunt (R_{sh}) and series resistance (R_s) of all devices, **Figure 6.2d**. We identify two dependence relationships between blend composition and the device performance which show the best compromise at a NiO_x:PEO ratio of 40 %wt. In the case of NiO_x content > 40 %wt, the device performance is limited by an increasing R_s. R_s is caused by injection barriers in the device, so we can infer that denser NiO_x nanoparticle layers are not favorable for efficient hole extraction from the solar cell. In the case of HTL blends with NiO_x content < 40 %wt, R_s values are relatively little affected by composition,

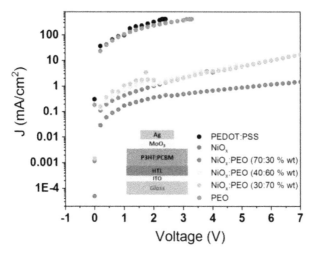

Figure 6.4: Unipolar (hole only) device with HTLs with different NiO$_x$ concentration.

however, R_{sh} strongly depends on composition with a maximum at 40%wt. We conclude that a further decrease in nanoparticle concentration < 40 %wt does not allow for the formation of a dense nanoparticle layer, thus providing energetically inferior paths for the photocurrent which leads to a decrease of the R_{sh} and consequently a reduction in the output of the solar cell. It can be therefore assessed that the best working blend, NiO$_x$:PEO 40%wt, is a compromise of these two tendencies.

All HTLs were annealed at 100°C and oxygen plasma treated prior to the deposition of the active layer. This is a necessary step for the formation of the more conductive species NiOOH by further oxidation during the plasma treatment and consequently for the optimized performance of the

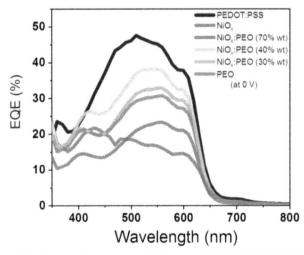

Figure 6.5: External quantum efficiency of P3HT:PC(60)BM cells at 0V (which is equivalent to short circuit current condition).

devices, as it showed in **Figure 6.3**.[119, 123, 127] The effect of the oxygen plasma on the HTL quality has been discussed more in detail in Section 4.3, evidencing that through the PEO etching by the plasma the NiO_x:PEO blends showed the properties necessary for a good quality NiO_x thin layer, i.e. thickness close to the one of a single layer of nanoparticles and the appropriate WF of ~5 eV.[55, 121]

In the same figure, we plotted for comparison a device on bare plasma-cleaned ITO (i.e. no HTL), showing a clear improvement in device performance with NiO_x as HTL, and a device with PEDOT:PSS, with a PCE of 3.00% that confirms the quality of the P3HT:PC_{60}BM active layer. The utilization of P3HT:PC_{60}BM as active layer material, although not exhibiting a high performance compared to state-of-the-art organic and perovskite-based PVs, was meant to offer a standard for the introduction of the processing approach of NiO_x by blending with a polymer. The characterization of the hole unipolar devices for different contents of NiO_x confirms that the presence of PEO in the NiO_x:PEO blends causes a higher hole current than neat NiO_x for all ratios of blends, as **Figure 6.4** shows. The hole injection ability of NiO_x containing HTLs is anyways around 3 orders of magnitude lower than PEDOT:PSS HTL. Interestingly, the neat PEO layer showed a high hole current, counterintuitively to the insulant nature of the polymer. The reason for that can be correlated to the etching of the PEO by the oxygen plasma treatment, which leaves behind ITO which is instead very efficient in injecting holes. [21, 24]

Figure 6.5 presents the EQE measurement at 0V, which represents the behavior in the photocurrent production efficiency observed in the devices. Interestingly, there is a general dimming in the spectral distribution of the P3HT photoresponse for the devices with neat NiO_x, while in the cases of the NiO_x:PEO blends the shoulder at around 420 nm of P3HT absorption becomes more defined. These results could be correlated with the conclusions drawn from the transient absorption analysis of P3HT:PC$_{60}$BM discussed in Section 4.3.2.4, which evidenced from the different charge transfer dynamics that small morphological changes in the P3HT:PC$_{60}$BM layer are induced by the underlying NiO_x:PEO HTL, increasing the crystallinity of P3HT and therefore giving the spectral photocurrent a more resolved peak structure. [157]

6.2.1 Inkjet-printed NiO$_x$:PEO in P3HT:PC$_{60}$BM solar cells

After considering the surface wettability (discussed in Section 4.3.2.6) and developing a printable ink formulation, devices with inkjet printed NiO$_x$ HTLs were fabricated. The fabrication by inkjet printing of layers from ethanol-based solutions is challenging due to the low viscosity and fast evaporation of the solvent, as the boiling temperature is T$_b$= 78.4 °C and the viscosity is 1.095 cP. [28, 30, 83, 84]

Therefore, for the fabrication of inkjet-printed layers, another solvent was incorporated in the system to tune the viscosity of the ink. Diethylene glycol (DEG) (T$_b$ = 197.3 °C, viscosity 35.7 cP) was added to the as-received NP suspension with a final proportion ethanol:DEG 1:3. The post-treatments of these layers included vacuum drying, annealing at 100°C and oxygen plasma treatment. The characteristics of devices fabricated with HTLs from the DEG-containing solutions are displayed in **Figure 6.6** and relevant parameters are summarized in **Table 6.1**. To ensure that the viscosity tuning by DEG addition was not the only responsible for the improved performance of the NiO$_x$ layer, spin-coated layers from the same ink were fabricated as well. Neat PEO and neat NiO$_x$ and three blends with different content of NiO$_x$ were fabricated to determine the influence of the printing technique on the device performance. In all cases, the inkjet printed HTLs resulted in the best performing devices with higher V$_{oc}$ and J$_{sc}$, and consequently PCEs. Furthermore, introducing DEG resulted

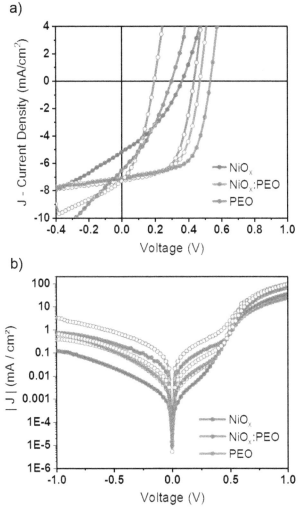

Figure 6.6: Current density vs Voltage characteristics under 100 mW/cm² (a) and in dark condition (b) for solar cells with HTL produced by inkjet printing (full symbols) and by spin coating (empty symbols) with DEG as additional solvent. The NiOx:PEO blend is optimized to a concentration 40:60 %wt.

in an improved device performance compared to devices

Table 6.1: Main device parameters for devices with inkjet-printed and spin-coated HTLs with DEG as additional solvent for increasing concentration of NiO$_x$.

	Jsc [mA/cm^2]	Voc [V]	Fill Factor	PCE [%]
Inkjet printed HTL				
NiO$_x$	-5.23 ± 0.71	0.37 ± 0.06	34.5 ± 0.3	0.69 ± 0.21
NiO$_x$:PEO 70:30%	-7.26 ± 0.13	0.52 ± 0.02	58.4 ± 6.4	2.19 ± 0.32
NiO$_x$:PEO 40:60%	-7.15 ± 0.22	0.54 ± 0.01	61.2 ± 2.5	2.37 ± 0.13
NiO$_x$:PEO 30:70%	N.A.	N.A.	N.A.	N.A.
PEO	-6.57 ± 0.44	0.31 ± 0.12	35.5 ± 8.2	0.76 ± 0.5
Spin-Coated HTL				
NiO$_x$	-2.81 ± 0.05	0.49 ± 0.01	19.2 ± 1.2	0.26 ± 0.04
NiO$_x$:PEO 70:30%	-3.37 ± 0.92	0.22 ± 0.06	23.5 ± 0.94	0.17 ± 0.07
NiO$_x$:PEO 40:60%	-7.09 ± 0.11	0.48 ± 0.02	50.6 ± 2.3	1.79 ± 0.23
NiO$_x$:PEO 30:70%	-7.60 ± 0.14	0.41 ± 0.06	44.2 ± 2.9	1.39 ± 0.32
PEO	-7.33 ± 0.23	0.21 ± 0.04	37.8 ± 3.1	0.56 ± 0.15

processed from ethanol-only HTLs shown in **Figure 6.2**. Due to its higher boiling point, DEG slows down the drying process, leading to a different film formation dynamics. For the inkjet printing process, a longer drying time provides the necessary time for the coalescence of the deposited drops. Notably, the results show as well that the inclusion of PEO is necessary to obtain the well performing of the NiO$_x$ HTLs, with an average efficiency for the optimized blend (NiO$_x$:PEO 40:60% wt) PCE = 2.37%.

The NiO$_x$:PEO 30:70% wt layer formation was not achievable by inkjet printing, possibly because of the clustering of the nanoparticles evidenced and discussed already through EDS-SEM (in Section 4.3.2.2) that didn't allow a sufficiently closed film coverage. The NiO_x:PEO 70:30% wt blend, when printed, has close performance compared to the optimal one.

The performance of the optimized HTL is comparable to the ones obtained in literature with NiO_x precursors (sol-gel method) that require a thermal treatment > 200°C.[126]

6.3 NiO$_x$:PEO as HTL for other active layers

To demonstrate that the NiO_x film can function as an effective HTL, organic solar cells have been fabricated and characterized with other active layers. As represented in Figure 6.1, PTB7:PC_{70}BM with a HOMO energy level of 5.1 eV, and P3HT:o-IDTBR as non-fullerene acceptor, were used to examine the effect of NiO_x:PEO film as an efficient HTL. These systems are interesting for being a low-bandgap polymer in the first case, and for being a novel high-performing active blend in the second case. Both active layer blends are known in the literature to be more performing than the reference P3HT:PC_{60}BM solar cells, with maximum reported efficiencies of 7.4% and 6.2%, respectively.[71, 72]

Figure 6.7 shows the IV curves under illumination of these devices, and their figures of merit are collected in **Table 6.2.** In all cases, the results were modest compared to the performances usually reported for these materials, even in the case of the PEDOT:PSS HTL used as reference, so that these examples have to be considered as a not-fully optimized proof of concept. For these devices, NiOx:PEO refers to the blend 40:60% wt. optimized for the

194

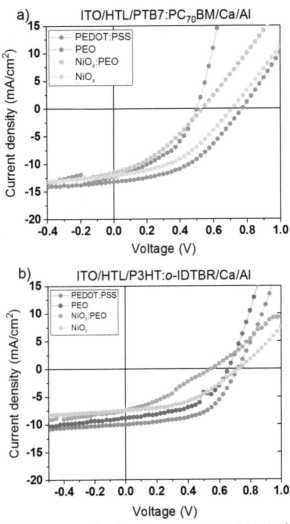

Figure 6.7: IV curves under illumination of PTB7:PC₇₀BM (a) and P3HT:o-IDTBR (b) based solar cells, with PEDOT:PSS, PEO, NiOₓ or NIOₓ:PEO as HTL.

P3HT:PCBM. Due to the scarce performance of the reference

Table 6.2: Main device parameters for devices with PTB7:PC70BM active layer with different HTLs for increasing concentration of NiOx.

	Jsc [mA/cm²]	Voc [V]	Fill Factor	PCE [%]
PEDOT:PSS	-13.24 ± 0.21	0.73 ± 0.02	47.2 ± 2.5	4.60 ± 0.29
PEO	-12.31 ± 0.32	0.48 ± 0.03	45.7 ± 4.0	2.71 ± 0.52
NiOx:PEO 40:60%	-11.52 ± 0.31	0.51 ± 0.01	37.3± 4.3	2.21 ± 0.31
NiOx	-12.22 ± 0.21	0.69 ± 0.02	44.5 ± 2.3	3.69 ± 0.23

Table 6.3: Main device parameters for devices with P3HT:o-IDTBR active layer with different HTLs for increasing concentration of NiOx.

	Jsc [mA/cm²]	Voc [V]	Fill Factor	PCE [%]
PEDOT:PSS	-10.03 ± 0.13	0.70 ± 0.02	56.6 ± 0.7	3.94 ± 0.15
PEO	-8.83	0.64	52	2.94
NiOx:PEO 40:60%	-7.42 ± 0.61	0.52 ± 0.04	35.4 ± 3.5	1.35 ± 0.14
NiOx	-7.49 ± 0.24	0.70 ± 0.02	45.1 ± 0.21	2.37 ± 0.03

devices, no further concentration was investigated at this point, but planned to be investigated in the future.

In the case of the PTB7:PC70BM (Figure 6.7a and Table 6.2), neat NiO_x as HTL has the closest performance compared to the PEDOT:PSS, with a V_{oc} of 0.69 V and an efficiency of 3.69%. This result suggested that for this active material a thicker HTL is better. The results showed the same energy alignment ability observed for P3HT, confirmed with low-bandgap polymer PTB7-based device. The main difference from the PEDOT:PSS HTL is in this case in the lower current produced, due most probably to the high resistivity of the thicker layer of NiO_x already evidenced and discussed for P3HT:PCBM devices.

In the case of the P3HT:o-IDTBR solar cells (Figure 6.7b and Table 6.3), the HTL with neat NiO_x outperformed again the NiO_x:PEO blend. It can be noted that concerning PEO as HTL, such device had such a low reproducibility that all the other devices fabricated resulted in shortcuts and didn't allow real device performance statistics. NiO_x shows the same V_{oc} as PEDOT:PSS, but once again allows only the extraction of a lower current resulting in overall lower efficiency.

In both cases, the blend NiO_x:PEO 40:60% wt didn't improve the efficiency of the devices. As further development one could try HTL blends with a higher content of NiO_x, resulting in thicker HTLs. Nonetheless, the neat NiO_x nanoparticle layer revealed a performance as HTL comparable to the one of PEDOT:PSS, especially as regards the final V_{oc} of the devices, demonstrating that NiO_x is applicable with different-bandgap polymeric donors in OPVs, although requiring further optimization.

6.4 NiO_x:PEO with Low Molecular Weight PEO as HTL

The effect of the molecular weight of PEO on the HTL film formation was investigated by fabricating devices with NiO_x:PEO blends using a very low molecular weight PEO, 400 instead of the high molecular weight (10^6) used in the previous sections.

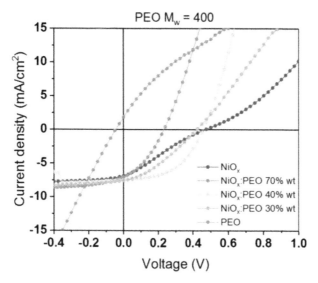

Figure 6.8: IV curves under illumination of P3HT:PC$_{60}$BM based solar cells as a function of different concentration of NiO$_x$ blended with low M$_w$ PEO as HTL, as closest to average of 4 devices.

Figure 6.8 shows the IV curves under illumination of these devices, while their figures of merit are collected in **Table 6.3**. The overall device performance is lower than the counterpart produced with high molecular weight PEO, suffering specifically of lower photocurrent and lower open circuit voltages. This can be attributed to defects in the HTL layer formation, as the shorter polymer chains don't allow good separation of the nanoparticles, leaving behind after the plasma etching a too clustered and consequently too resistive NiO$_x$ film. Interestingly, also for these devices the blend NiO$_x$:PEO 40:60% wt is neatly better performing than the single components and the other blends, with a

Table 6.3: Main device parameters for devices for increasing concentration of NiO$_x$ and PEO (Mw 400), as average of 4 devices.

	Jsc [mA/cm²]	Voc [V]	Fill Factor	PCE [%]
NiO$_x$	-2.19 ± 0.51	0.41 ± 0.01	15.4 ± 0.6	0.14 ± 0.05
NiO$_x$:PEO 70:30%	-6.98 ± 0.35	0.33 ± 0.03	34.5 ± 1.7	0.56 ± 0.04
NiO$_x$:PEO 40:60%	-7.51 ± 0.16	0.43 ± 0.02	52.9 ± 6.3	1.72 ± 0.25
NiO$_x$:PEO 30:70%	-7.54 ± 0.22	0.40 ± 0.02	34.4 ± 2.6	1.06 ± 0.16
PEO	1.85 ± 0.21	-0.02 ± 0.01	22.8 ± 5.4	0.004 ± 0.2

maximum efficiency of 1.72%. The reason for this can be ascribed to the optimized compromise between nanoparticle dispersion, minimum thickness and coverage quality observed for the counterpart with high molecular weight PEO, whose properties are discussed in more detail in Chapter 5. Concerning neat low M$_w$ PEO as HTL, it has been reported before several times its successful employment as ETL with hole blocking properties. [77–79] Therefore, it's not surprising to see that the device has a very poor device performance, with the J-V characteristic actually in the first quadrant, in opposition to the regular case. Thus, these devices performance confirmed that in order to get an optimal NiO$_x$ HTL the dispersing polymer needs to have long chains in order to guarantee proper distribution of the nanoparticles before being etched by the oxygen plasma.

6.5 Conclusions

In this chapter, solution-processed organic solar cells with three bulk heterojunctions as active materials were fabricated to test the quality of different NiO_x:PEO blends as hole transport layer. It was demonstrated that blending the NiO_x nanoparticles with high molecular weight PEO offers a simple, low-temperature approach for the solution processing of NiO_x that applies as well for inkjet printing. PEO was utilized as a processing additive, which improves NiO_x film formation and was subsequently be removed prior to device fabrication.

The resulting $P3HT:PC_{60}BM$ devices showed a maximum of efficiency for the blend NiO_x:PEO 40:60%wt. Interestingly, the optimal ratio between NiO_x and PEO is preserved when the layers are produced both by spin coating and inkjet printing. The best working devices were the ones with the NiOx:PEO HTL produced by inkjet printing, with a performance comparable to the results obtained in literature for inkjet-printed devices that required a thermal treatment at >250°C. The utilization of P3HT:PCBM as active layer material, although not exhibiting a high performance compared to state-of-the-art OPVs, offers an optimum standard for the introduction of the presented HTL processing approach.

As a proof of concept, devices were produced with alternative, higher efficient bulk heterojunctions $PTB7:PC_{70}BM$ and P3HT:o-IDTBR. In this case, the neat NiO_x was observed to be more performing than the NiO_x:PEO blends. NiO_x as HTL revealed a performance comparable to the one of the reference PEDOT:PSS HTL, especially in terms of the V_{oc} of the devices. Therefore, the compatibility of this material with different-bandgap polymeric donors in OPVs. Nonetheless, this kind of solar cells was not fully engineered and need further optimization.

Other P3HT:PC$_{60}$BM devices were produced by using a PEO with low molecular weight, showing overall lower device performances. These results confirmed that in order to get an optimal NiO$_x$ HTL the dispersing polymer needs to have long chains in order to guarantee proper distribution of the nanoparticles before being etched by the oxygen plasma. Also, in the case of these devices the blend NiO$_x$:PEO 40:60% wt is neatly better performing than the single components and the other blends.

Therefore, the low-temperature process reported here by blending NiO$_x$ with a sacrificial polymer additive provides an excellent low-temperature alternative that enables inkjet printing of NiO$_x$ HTLs for solution-processed photovoltaics application without requiring high-temperature post-treatment, resulting in device architectures more suitable for the industrial processing of printed devices on plastic substrates.

7 Conclusions and outlook

One of the most important research directions in the field solution-processed organic electronics lies in the area interface engineering, as organic optoelectronic devices are generally constructed in a multilayer architecture. Particularly, interlayers for carrier injection and extraction from and to the electrodes are crucial components which choice, arrangement, and quality determine the final device architecture and device performance. Along with the obvious energetic considerations in relation to the semiconducting active layer, their processability is key to form high-quality electronic interfaces.

This thesis aims to contribute to the engineering of interfaces in organic optoelectronic devices by investigating the fabrication and properties of solution-processed nanocomposite interlayers. Specifically, the nanocomposites presented herein are based on transition metal oxide nanoparticles and polymers, as a way to combine an optimized work function, transport and reliability of nanoparticles with the processability and versatility of polymers. Three nanocomposite systems were investigated as interlayers in OLEDs and OPV: ZnO and poly(sulfobetaine methacrylate) (ZnO/PSBMA), NiO_x and poly(ethylene oxide) (NiO_x:PEO) and ZnO with poly(ethyleneimine) (ZnO:PEI). The experimental results are reported in Chapters 4-6 where the processing properties of the different interlayers, the contact formation between emitter, interlayer and cathode as well as the resulting device properties were investigated and optimized.

Chapter 4 presents the electronic, optical and morphological characterization of the different metal oxide nanoparticles:polymer nanocomposites thin films. In Chapter 5 solution-processed OLEDs based on the PPV derivative SY and the fluorene derivative F8BT as active materials were fabricated to test the quality of the three different nanoparticle-polymer systems as charge injection layers. Furthermore, Chapter 6 presents solution-processed organic solar cells with three different bulk heterojunction systems in combination with NiO_x:PEO blends as a hole transport layer.

The first system investigated is the bilayer PSBMA/ZnO. In Chapter 4, AFM images showed that PSBMA mitigates the roughness of the ZnO nanoparticles and achieved an overall smooth and even topography. Kelvin Probe measurement demonstrated that the WF of ZnO is reduced of up to 0.3 eV and the one of Al up to 0.2 eV compared to that of the pristine materials after being covered by a thin layer of PSBMA. Through photoelectron spectroscopy measurements the WF measurement was confirmed and the optimal thickness for PSBMA was assessed to be around 2 nm. FT-IRRAS spectroscopy elucidated that PSBMA replaces the adsorbates present on a pristine ZnO surface. As the adsorbates on the nanoparticulate ZnO mostly contain oxygen, the replacement led to a reduction of trap states at the interface. ZnO/PSBMA bilayers were then employed as electron injection layer for both SY and F8BT OLEDs in Chapter 5. The maximum current efficiency of such OLEDs with a value of approx. 1.5 cd/A was clearly above the current efficiency of OLEDs with pure ZnO cathode, which was only about 0.1 cd/A. The characterization of the unipolar devices for both charge carriers confirms that the presence of PSBMA in the device causes a lower hole current and three orders of magnitude higher electron current, respectively. Finally, was found that PSBMA not only reduces the WF of Al and ZnO, enabling lower operational voltages but also serves as a surface trap passivation for ZnO, stabilizing the device under operating conditions. This was evidenced by running multiple consecutive voltage bias ramps and applying a bias before measuring the luminance.

The second system examined is NiO_x:PEO blends. In Chapter 4 it was demonstrated that high molecular weight polyethylene oxide can help to disperse the nanoparticles hindering their aggregation after deposition without compromising film functionality. Through Kelvin Probe, Contact Angle measurements, XPS, and TEM it was assessed that the presence of PEO was beneficial for a better tunability of the NiO_x film thickness and morphology. Through SEM and TEM the nanoparticles appeared homogenously dispersed in the PEO, and thanks to XPS analysis it was observed that after the deposition the PEO gets etched by oxygen plasma treatment and thus acts as a removable passive matrix for the deposition of the NiO_x nanoparticles. The produced NiO_x:PEO blends, after the oxygen plasma treatment, showed the properties necessary for a good quality NiO_x thin layer, i.e. thickness close to the one of a single layer of nanoparticles and the appropriate WF of ~5 eV. In Chapter 5 NiO_x:PEO blends were employed as a hole injection layer in SY based OLEDs. It was demonstrated that the NiO_x film thickness must be as low as possible in order to reach the highest possible efficiency. Lastly, blending NiO_x with PEO allows the formation of the best working hole injection layers, with a maximum efficiency of 1.3 cd/A. The sharp increase in all the figures of merit confirms that the best working HIL has an optimal thickness of around 10 nm, that it requires an oxygen plasma treatment and that its formation is facilitated by mixing the nanoparticle dispersion with PEO. In Chapter 6, solution-processed organic solar cells with three bulk heterojunctions as active materials were fabricated to test the quality of different NiO_x:PEO blends as the hole transport layer. The resulting P3HT:PC$_{60}$BM devices showed a maximum of efficiency for the blend NiO_x:PEO 40:60%wt. Interestingly, the optimal ratio between NiO_x and PEO is preserved when the layers are produced both by spin coating and inkjet printing. The best working devices were the ones with the NiO_x:PEO hole transport layer produced by inkjet printing, with a performance comparable to the results obtained in literature for inkjet-printed devices that required a thermal treatment at >250°C. As a proof of concept, devices were produced with alternative, higher efficient bulk heterojunctions PTB7:PC_{70}BM and P3HT:o-IDTBR. In this case, the neat NiO_x was observed to be better performing than the NiO_x:PEO blends and revealed a performance comparable to the one of the reference PEDOT:PSS HTL, with comparable values of V_{oc}. Therefore, the compatibility of this material with different-bandgap polymeric donors in OPVs is demonstrated. Nonetheless, this kind of solar cells was not fully engineered and need further optimization. Further P3HT:PC_{60}BM devices were produced utilizing a low molecular weight PEO as NiO_x processing additive, showing overall lower device performances. These results confirmed that in order to get an optimal NiO_x hole transport layer the dispersing polymer needs to have long chains in order to guarantee proper distribution of the nanoparticles before being etched by the oxygen plasma. Also, in the case of these devices the blend NiO_x:PEO 40:60% wt proved to be better performing than the single components and the other blends.

The third and last system examined is ZnO:PEI, a well-known system for electron injection in OLEDs. In Chapter 4 the ZnO:PEI layers are studied through Kelvin Probe and by steady-state and transient photoluminescence spectroscopy, while in Chapter 5 a novel characterization method for OLEDs is proposed, where the effect of the electron injection layer is studied through ultra-fast pump-probe spectroscopy, giving new insight on the mechanisms happening at the interfaces ZnO/SuperYellow and ZnO:PEI/SuperYellow in operating device conditions. The

207

transient and steady-state photoluminescence study of the ZnO:PEI/SY interface indicate that upon excitation of the SY electron injection takes place from the SY towards the ZnO:PEI blend, confirming that the injection barrier for this interlayer is lower than the neat ZnO nanoparticles, while the contact PEI/SY is not found to cause quenching of the SY emission, suggesting that no electron transfer process happens between SY and PEI. From the transient absorption study it was evidenced that neat ZnO nanoparticles actually might be an emission quenching source for the SY. In contrast, ZnO:PEI, induces slower dynamics of stimulated emissions in SY that can be correlated with increased exciton population formed by charge injection. The devices used for transient absorption spectroscopy were as well characterized by L-I-V measurement, confirming the high performance of ZnO:PEI as EIL with an efficiency of up to 8.78 cd/A.

In summary, this work represents a significant progress in the development of efficient solution-processable interlayers for multilayer optoelectronic devices. It was demonstrated that the great potential of the nanoparticle:polymer nanocomposites approach presented in this thesis addressed a number of open problems that still need attention before fully solution-processed or printed organic electronics devices can meet the efficiency and lifetime requirements of commercial products. The investigated materials presented in this work achieved good OLED and high OPV efficiencies. ZnO combined with PSBMA evidenced for the first time the ability of PSBMA to intervene on the interface properties of ZnO nanoparticles. By using a composite EIL consisting of PEI and ZnO nanoparticles, it was possible to for the first time to investigate the dynamics of charge injection through pump-probe spectroscopy in devices under operation. By adding a PEO as an additive, it was possible to produce high quality NiO_x layer by inkjet printing without the requirement of a high temperature post-treatment.

Due to the simplicity of fabrication, the low temperature of post-treatment and the interesting interface properties, it is expected that the approach reported here could be applicable to a wider range of hybrid systems and interfaces in multilayer optoelectronic devices, resulting in device architectures more suitable for the industrial processing of printed devices on plastic substrates. In addition, the identified correlations between the structure of the investigated materials, their film formation properties and their behavior as interlayers can serve as a helpful orientation for the design of even better nanocomposite materials in the future.

8 Appendix

a. Processing parameters

Material	Formulation	Speed	Atmosphere	Annealing	Thickness
PEDOT:PSS	Heraeus PVP Al 4083	3800 rpm 35 s	Air	140°C 10 min	~40 nm
SuperYellow	Merck PDY-132, 5g/l Toluene	2000 rpm 60s	N₂ (Glovebox)	115°C 30 min	~70 nm
F8BT	Ossila, 5 g/l Toluene	2000 rpm 60s	N₂ (Glovebox)	120°C 10 min	~70 nm
P3HT:PCBM	Sigma Aldrich, 99% rr; Solenne 1:0.9 20 g/l DCB	800 rpm 120s	N₂ (Glovebox)	130°C 15 min	~90 nm
P3HT:o-IDTBR	Sigma Aldrich, 99% rr; 1-Materials 1:1 20 g/l DCB	1000 rpm 120s	N₂ (Glovebox)	130°C 15 min	~80 nm
PTB7:PCBM	1-Materials 1:1.5 20 g/l DCB	1000 rpm 120s	N₂ (Glovebox)	130°C 15 min	~80 nm
ZnO	Nanograde N10 diluted 1:3,5 Isopropanol	4000 rpm 45s	N₂ (Glovebox), Air	150°C 5 min	~16 nm
ZnO:PEI	Nanograde N10, Sigma Aldrich 7:1 Isopropanol	4000 rpm 45s	N₂ (Glovebox)	120°C 10 min	~19 nm
PEI	Sigma Aldrich, 0.05g/L Isopropanol	5000 rpm 45s	N₂ (Glovebox)	120°C 10min	~2 nm
PSBMA	Synthetized in [75] 0.1-2 g/L TFE	2000 rpm 40s	N₂ (Glovebox)	120°C 10min	~2 nm
NiOx	Nanograde P20 Ethanol	2000 rpm 40s	Air	100°C 10min	~15 nm
NiOx:PEO	Nanograde P20; Sigma Aldrich, Ethanol	2000 rpm 40s	Air	100°C 10min	~10 nm
PEO	Sigma Aldrich 1g/L Ethanol	2000 rpm 40s	Air	100°C 10min	~2 nm
NiOx:PEO Inkjet Ink	See above, + 3 vol DEG	2000 rpm 40s	Air	Vacuum, 100°C 10min	~10 nm

List of Abbreviations

a.u.	arbitrary units
AFM	Atomic Force Microscopy
BHJ	Bulk Hetero-Junction
CIE	International Commission on Illumination *(Comission Internationale de l'Éclairage)*
DAS	Decay Associated Spectra
DOS	Density of states
E_F	Fermi Energy
E_{Vac}	Vacuum Energy
EA	Electronic Affinity
EBL	Electron Blocking Layer
EDS	Energy-dispersive X-ray spectroscopy
EIL	Electron Injection Layer
EL	Electroluminescence
EMU	External Mounting Unit
EQE	External Quantum Efficiency
ETL	Electron Transport Layer
FF	Fill Factor
FT-IRRAS	Fourier Transform InfraRed Reflection Absorption Spectroscopy
GSB	Ground State Bleaching

213

HBL	Hole Blocking Layer
HIL	Hole Injection Layer
HTL	Hole Transport Layer
HOMO	Highest Occupied Molecular Orbital
IP	Ionization Potential
ISC	InterSystem-Crossing
IV	Current Density-Voltage
Jsc	Short-circuit Current
LCAO	Linear Combination of Atomic Orbitals
LCD	Liquid Crystal Display
LIV	Luminance-Current density-Voltage
LUMO	Lowest Unoccupied Molecular Orbital
M_w	Molecular Weight
OFET	Organic Field Effect Transistor
OLED	Organic Light-Emitting Diode
OPV	Organic solar cell (Organic PhotoVoltaics)
PCE	Power Conversion Efficiency
PES	PhotoElectron Spectroscopy
PIA	Photo Induced Absorption
PL	Photoluminescence
rms	root mean square (roughness)
rpm	rotations per minute

SAM	Self-Assembled Monolayer
SC	Spin-Coating
SE	Stimulated Emission
SEM	Scanning Electron Microscopy
SFE	Surface Free Energy
SMU	Source-Measuring-Unit
TA	Transient Absorption
TADF	Thermally Activated Delayed Fluorescence
T_b	Boiling temperature
TCSPC	Time Correlated Single Photon Counting
TEM	Transmission Electron Microscopy
UPS	Ultraviolet Photoelectron Spectroscopy
UV	Ultraviolet spectral range
UV-Vis	Ultraviolet and visual spectral range
Vis	Visual spectral range
V_{oc}	Open-circuit Voltage
Von	Turn-on Voltage
XPS	X-Ray Photoelectron Spectroscopy

Bibliography

1.   Koezuka H, Tsumura A, Ando T (1987) Field-effect transistor
      with polythiophene thin film. Synth Met 18:699–704.
      https://doi.org/10.1016/0379-6779(87)90964-7

2.   Sirringhaus H (2005) Device physics of solution-processed
      organic field-effect transistors. Adv Mater 17:2411–2425.
      https://doi.org/10.1002/adma.200501152

3.   Quinn JTE, Zhu J, Li X, et al (2017) Recent progress in the
      development of n-type organic semiconductors for organic field
      effect transistors. J Mater Chem C 5:8654–8681.
      https://doi.org/10.1039/C7TC01680H

4.   Tang CW (1986) Two-layer organic photovoltaic cell. Appl Phys
      Lett 48:183–185. https://doi.org/10.1063/1.96937

5.   (2019) Heliatek GmbH. https://www.heliatek.com/en/

6.   (2019) Opvious GmbH. http://www.opvius.com/

7.   (2019) NREL Photovoltaic Efficiency Chart.
      https://www.nrel.gov/pv/cell-efficiency.html

8.   Xue R, Zhang J, Li Y, Li Y (2018) Organic Solar Cell Materials
      toward Commercialization. Small 14:1801793.
      https://doi.org/10.1002/smll.201801793

9.   Tang CW, VanSlyke SA (1987) Organic electroluminescent
      diodes. Appl Phys Lett 51:913–915.
      https://doi.org/10.1063/1.98799

10.   Chen H-W, Lee J-H, Lin B-Y, et al (2018) Liquid crystal display
      and organic light-emitting diode display: present status and
      future perspectives. Light Sci Appl 7:17168.
      https://doi.org/10.1038/lsa.2017.168

11.   Tyan Y-S (2011) Organic light-emitting-diode lighting overview.
      J Photonics Energy 1:011009.
      https://doi.org/10.1117/1.3529412

12. Li X, Zhang W, Usman K, Fang J (2018) Small Molecule Interlayers in Organic Solar Cells. Adv Energy Mater 8:1702730. https://doi.org/10.1002/aenm.201702730

13. Koch N (2007) Organic electronic devices and their functional interfaces. ChemPhysChem 8:1438–1455. https://doi.org/10.1002/cphc.200700177

14. Ma H, Yip H-L, Huang F, Jen AK-Y (2010) Interface Engineering for Organic Electronics. Adv Funct Mater 20:1371–1388. https://doi.org/10.1002/adfm.200902236

15. Lai TH, Tsang SW, Manders JR, et al (2013) Properties of interlayer for organic photovoltaics. Mater Today 16:424–432. https://doi.org/10.1016/j.mattod.2013.10.001

16. Yeo JS, Kang M, Jung YS, et al (2016) In-depth considerations for better polyelectrolytes as interfacial materials in polymer solar cells. Nano Energy 21:26–38. https://doi.org/10.1016/j.nanoen.2016.01.003

17. Alt M, Schinke J, Hillebrandt S, et al (2014) Processing follows function: Pushing the formation of self-assembled monolayers to high-throughput compatible time scales. ACS Appl Mater Interfaces 6:20234–20241. https://doi.org/10.1021/am5057689

18. Zhou Y, Fuentes-Hernandez C, Shim J, et al (2012) A Universal Method to Produce Low-Work Function Electrodes for Organic Electronics. Science (80-) 336:327–332. https://doi.org/10.1126/science.1218829

19. Tokito S, Noda K, Taga Y (1996) Metal oxides as a hole-injecting layer for an organic electroluminescent device. J Phys D Appl Phys 29:2750–2753. https://doi.org/10.1088/0022-3727/29/11/004

20. Qiu C, Xie Z, Chen H, et al (2003) Comparative study of metal or oxide capped indium–tin oxide anodes for organic light-emitting diodes. J Appl Phys 93:3253–3258. https://doi.org/10.1063/1.1556184

21. Zilberberg K, Meyer J, Riedl T (2013) Solution processed metal-oxides for organic electronic devices. J Mater Chem C 1:4796.

https://doi.org/10.1039/c3tc30930d

22. Chiba T, Pu Y-J, Kido J (2015) Solution-processable electron injection materials for organic light-emitting devices. J Mater Chem C 3:11567–11576. https://doi.org/10.1039/C5TC02421H

23. Chen S, Manders JR, Tsang S-W, So F (2012) Metal oxides for interface engineering in polymer solar cells. J Mater Chem 22:24202. https://doi.org/10.1039/c2jm33838f

24. Li N, Stubhan T, Krantz J, et al (2014) A universal method to form the equivalent ohmic contact for efficient solution-processed organic tandem solar cells. J Mater Chem A 2:14896–14902. https://doi.org/10.1039/c4ta03182b

25. Chu C-W, Li S-H, Chen C-W, et al (2005) High-performance organic thin-film transistors with metal oxide/metal bilayer electrode. Appl Phys Lett 87:193508. https://doi.org/10.1063/1.2126140

26. Wang ZB, Helander MG, Qiu J, et al (2011) Unlocking the full potential of organic light-emitting diodes on flexible plastic. Nat Photonics 5:753–757. https://doi.org/10.1038/nphoton.2011.259

27. Steirer KX, Ndione PF, Widjonarko NE, et al (2011) Enhanced efficiency in plastic solar cells via energy matched solution processed NiO x interlayers. Adv Energy Mater 1:813–820. https://doi.org/10.1002/aenm.201100234

28. Gebauer JS, Mackert V, Ognjanović S, Winterer M (2018) Tailoring metal oxide nanoparticle dispersions for inkjet printing. J Colloid Interface Sci 526:400–409. https://doi.org/10.1016/j.jcis.2018.05.006

29. Glynn C, O'Dwyer C (2017) Solution Processable Metal Oxide Thin Film Deposition and Material Growth for Electronic and Photonic Devices. Adv Mater Interfaces 4:. https://doi.org/10.1002/admi.201600610

30. Liu X, Tarn T-J, Huang F, Fan J (2015) Recent advances in inkjet printing synthesis of functional metal oxides. Particuology 19:1–13. https://doi.org/10.1016/j.partic.2014.05.001

31.   Bouclé J, Ravirajan P, Nelson J (2007) Hybrid polymer-metal oxide thin films for photovoltaic applications. J Mater Chem 17:3141–3153. https://doi.org/10.1039/b706547g

32.   Ginzburg V V (2010) Nanoparticle / Polymer Blends : Theory and Modeling Table of Contents. In: Building

33.   Köhler A, Bässler H (2015) Electronic processes in organic semiconductors: An introduction. Wiley-VCH Verlag GmbH & Co. KGaA, Weinheim, Germany

34.   Liang J, Ying L, Huang F, Cao Y (2016) Recent advances in high performance solution processed WOLEDs for solid-state lighting. J Mater Chem C 4:10993–11006. https://doi.org/10.1039/C6TC03468C

35.   Klauk H (2012) Organic Electronics II. Wiley-VCH Verlag GmbH & Co. KGaA, Weinheim, Germany

36.   Liu Y, Li C, Ren Z, et al (2018) All-organic thermally activated delayed fluorescence materials for organic light-emitting diodes. Nat Rev Mater 3:18020. https://doi.org/10.1038/natrevmats.2018.20

37.   Yang Z, Mao Z, Xie Z, et al (2017) Recent advances in organic thermally activated delayed fluorescence materials. Chem Soc Rev 46:915–1016. https://doi.org/10.1039/C6CS00368K

38.   Klauk H (2012) Organic Electronics II: More Materials and Applications. Wiley

39.   Mikhnenko O V., Blom PWM, Nguyen T-Q (2015) Exciton diffusion in organic semiconductors. Energy Environ Sci 8:1867–1888. https://doi.org/10.1039/C5EE00925A

40.   Coropceanu V, Cornil J, da Silva Filho DA, et al (2007) Charge Transport in Organic Semiconductors. Chem Rev 107:926–952. https://doi.org/10.1021/cr050140x

41.   Facchetti A (2007) Semiconductors for organic transistors. Mater Today 10:28–37. https://doi.org/10.1016/S1369-7021(07)70017-2

42.   Ishii H, Sugiyama K, Ito E, Seki K (1999) Energy Level Alignment

and Interfacial Electronic Structures at Organic/Metal and Organic/Organic Interfaces. Adv Mater 11:605–625. https://doi.org/10.1002/(SICI)1521-4095(199906)11:8<605::AID-ADMA605>3.0.CO;2-Q

43.   Schlaf R, Lang O, Pettenkofer C, Jaegermann W (1999) Band lineup of layered semiconductor heterointerfaces prepared by van der Waals epitaxy: Charge transfer correction term for the electron affinity rule. J Appl Phys 85:2732–2753. https://doi.org/10.1063/1.369590

44.   Kahn A, Koch N, Gao W (2003) Electronic structure and electrical properties of interfaces between metals and ?-conjugated molecular films. J Polym Sci Part B Polym Phys 41:2529–2548. https://doi.org/10.1002/polb.10642

45.   Nonnenmacher M, O'Boyle MP, Wickramasinghe HK (1991) Kelvin probe force microscopy. Springer Berlin Heidelberg, Berlin, Heidelberg

46.   Hofmann S (2013) Auger- and X-Ray Photoelectron Spectroscopy in Materials Science. Springer Berlin Heidelberg, Berlin, Heidelberg, Heidelberg

47.   Yin Z, Wei J, Zheng Q (2016) Interfacial Materials for Organic Solar Cells: Recent Advances and Perspectives. Adv Sci 3:1–37. https://doi.org/10.1002/advs.201500362

48.   Berntsen AJM, van de Weijer P, Croonen Y, et al (1998) Stability of polymer light-emitting diodes. Philips J Res 51:511–525. https://doi.org/10.1016/S0165-5817(98)00021-7

49.   Schlisske S, Held M, Rödlmeier T, et al (2018) Substrate-Independent Surface Energy Tuning via Siloxane Treatment for Printed Electronics. Langmuir 34:5964–5970. https://doi.org/10.1021/acs.langmuir.8b00304

50.   Stolz S, Lemmer U, Hernandez-Sosa G, Mankel E (2018) Correlation of Device Performance and Fermi Level Shift in the Emitting Layer of Organic Light-Emitting Diodes with Amine-Based Electron Injection Layers. ACS Appl Mater Interfaces 10:8877–8884. https://doi.org/10.1021/acsami.7b16352

51.   de Boer B, Hadipour A, Mandoc MM, et al (2005) Tuning of

Metal Work Functions with Self-Assembled Monolayers. Adv Mater 17:621–625. https://doi.org/10.1002/adma.200401216

52. Alt M, Jesper M, Schinke J, et al (2016) The Swiss-Army-Knife Self-Assembled Monolayer: Improving Electron Injection, Stability, and Wettability of Metal Electrodes with a One-Minute Process. Adv Funct Mater 26:3172–3178. https://doi.org/10.1002/adfm.201505386

53. Liu Z, Zhu A, Cai F, et al (2017) Nickel oxide nanoparticles for efficient hole transport in p-i-n and n-i-p perovskite solar cells. J Mater Chem A 5:6597–6605. https://doi.org/10.1039/C7TA01593C

54. Greiner MT, Chai L, Helander MG, et al (2012) Transition Metal Oxide Work Functions: The Influence of Cation Oxidation State and Oxygen Vacancies. Adv Funct Mater 22:4557–4568. https://doi.org/10.1002/adfm.201200615

55. Greiner MT, Lu ZH (2013) Thin-film metal oxides in organic semiconductor devices: Their electronic structures, work functions and interfaces. NPG Asia Mater 5:e55-16. https://doi.org/10.1038/am.2013.29

56. Corr SA (2016) Metal oxide nanoparticles. SPR Nanosci 3:31–56. https://doi.org/10.1039/9781782623717-00031

57. Griffith JS, Orgel LE (1957) Ligand-field theory. Q Rev Chem Soc 11:381. https://doi.org/10.1039/qr9571100381

58. Meyer J, Shu A, Kröger M, Kahn A (2010) Effect of contamination on the electronic structure and hole-injection properties of MoO3/organic semiconductor interfaces. Appl Phys Lett 96:133308. https://doi.org/10.1063/1.3374333

59. Lany S, Osorio-Guillén J, Zunger A (2007) Origins of the doping asymmetry in oxides: Hole doping in NiO versus electron doping in ZnO. Phys Rev B 75:241203. https://doi.org/10.1103/PhysRevB.75.241203

60. Fergus JW (2003) Doping and defect association in oxides for use in oxygen sensors. J Mater Sci 38:4259–4270. https://doi.org/10.1023/A:1026318712367

61. Morfa AJ, Kirkwood N, Karg M, et al (2011) Effect of defects on the behavior of ZnO nanoparticle FETs. J Phys Chem C 115:8312–8315. https://doi.org/10.1021/jp200208k

62. Chen X, Liu Y, Ma Q (2018) Recent advances in quantum dot-based electrochemiluminescence sensors. J Mater Chem C 6:942–959. https://doi.org/10.1039/C7TC05474B

63. Aliofkhazraei M (2015) Handbook of nanoparticles. Springer International Publishing

64. Yu X, Marks TJ, Facchetti A (2016) Metal oxides for optoelectronic applications. Nat Mater 15:383–396. https://doi.org/10.1038/nmat4599

65. Zhang C, Zhang J, Hao Y, et al (2011) A simple and efficient solar cell parameter extraction method from a single current-voltage curve. J Appl Phys 110:064504. https://doi.org/10.1063/1.3632971

66. Reese MO, Gevorgyan SA, Jørgensen M, et al (2011) Consensus stability testing protocols for organic photovoltaic materials and devices. Sol Energy Mater Sol Cells 95:1253–1267. https://doi.org/10.1016/j.solmat.2011.01.036

67. (2019) OLED Lighting (OLED-info). https://www.oled-info.com/oled-lighting

68. Sandström A, Matyba P, Edman L (2010) Yellow-green light-emitting electrochemical cells with long lifetime and high efficiency. Appl Phys Lett 96:053303. https://doi.org/10.1063/1.3299018

69. McNeill CR, Greenham NC (2009) Conjugated-Polymer Blends for Optoelectronics. Adv Mater 21:3840–3850. https://doi.org/10.1002/adma.200900783

70. Luther J, Nast M, Fisch MN, et al (2012) Solar Technology. In: Ullmann's Encyclopedia of Industrial Chemistry. Wiley-VCH Verlag GmbH & Co. KGaA, Weinheim, Germany

71. He Z, Zhong C, Su S, et al (2012) Enhanced power-conversion efficiency in polymer solar cells using an inverted device structure. Nat Photonics 6:591–595.

223

https://doi.org/10.1038/nphoton.2012.190

72.	Holliday S, Ashraf RS, Wadsworth A, et al (2016) High-efficiency and air-stable P3HT-based polymer solar cells with a new non-fullerene acceptor. Nat Commun 7:1–11. https://doi.org/10.1038/ncomms11585

73.	Yan C, Barlow S, Wang Z, et al (2018) Non-fullerene acceptors for organic solar cells. Nat Rev Mater 3:1–19. https://doi.org/10.1038/natrevmats.2018.3

74.	Chiba T, Pu Y-J, Kido J (2015) Solution-processable electron injection materials for organic light-emitting devices. J Mater Chem C 3:11567–11576. https://doi.org/10.1039/C5TC02421H

75.	Lee H, Puodziukynaite E, Zhang Y, et al (2015) Poly(sulfobetaine methacrylate)s as Electrode Modi fi ers for Inverted Organic Electronics. J Am Chem Soc 137:540–549. https://doi.org/10.1021/ja512148d

76.	Chen HC, Lin SW, Jiang JM, et al (2015) Solution-processed zinc oxide/polyethylenimine nanocomposites as tunable electron transport layers for highly efficient bulk heterojunction polymer solar cells. ACS Appl Mater Interfaces 7:6273–6281. https://doi.org/10.1021/acsami.5b00521

77.	Arya A, Sharma AL (2017) Insights into the use of polyethylene oxide in energy storage/conversion devices: a critical review. J Phys D Appl Phys 50:443002. https://doi.org/10.1088/1361-6463/aa8675

78.	Ferenczi TAM, Müller C, Bradley DDC, et al (2011) Organic semiconductor: Insulator polymer ternary blends for photovoltaics. Adv Mater 23:4093–4097. https://doi.org/10.1002/adma.201102100

79.	Shao S, Zheng K, Pullerits T, Zhang F (2013) Enhanced performance of inverted polymer solar cells by using poly(ethylene oxide)-modified ZnO as an electron transport layer. ACS Appl Mater Interfaces 5:380–385. https://doi.org/10.1021/am302408w

80.	Huang J, Miller PF, Wilson JS, et al (2005) Investigation of the

Effects of Doping and Post-Deposition Treatments on the Conductivity, Morphology, and Work Function of Poly(3,4-ethylenedioxythiophene)/Poly(styrene sulfonate) Films. Adv Funct Mater 15:290–296. https://doi.org/10.1002/adfm.200400073

81. Stöcker T, Köhler A, Moos R (2012) Why does the electrical conductivity in PEDOT:PSS decrease with PSS content? A study combining thermoelectric measurements with impedance spectroscopy. J Polym Sci Part B Polym Phys 50:976–983. https://doi.org/10.1002/polb.23089

82. Stolz S, Zhang Y, Lemmer U, et al (2017) Degradation Mechanisms in Organic Light-Emitting Diodes with Polyethylenimine as a Solution-Processed Electron Injection Layer. ACS Appl Mater Interfaces 9:2776–2785. https://doi.org/10.1021/acsami.6b15062

83. Derby B (2010) Inkjet Printing of Functional and Structural Materials: Fluid Property Requirements, Feature Stability, and Resolution. Annu Rev Mater Res 40:395–414. https://doi.org/10.1146/annurev-matsci-070909-104502

84. Cummins G, Desmulliez MPY (2012) Inkjet printing of conductive materials: A review. Circuit World 38:193–213. https://doi.org/10.1108/03056121211280413

85. Tompkins HG, Irene EA (2006) Handbook of Ellipsometry. Springer Berlin Heidelberg

86. Giessibl FJ (2003) Advances in atomic force microscopy. Rev Mod Phys 75:949–983. https://doi.org/10.1103/RevModPhys.75.949

87. Stokes DJ (2008) Principles and Practice of Variable Pressure/Environmental Scanning Electron Microscopy (VP-ESEM). John Wiley & Sons, Ltd, Chichester, UK

88. Goldstein JI, Newbury DE, Echlin P, et al (2003) Scanning Electron Microscopy and X-ray Microanalysis. Springer US, Boston, MA

89. Egerton RF (2006) Physical Principles of Electron Microscopy. Springer US, Boston, MA

90. Klein A, Mayer T, Thissen A, Jaegermann W (2012) Photoelectron Spectroscopy in Materials Science and Physical Chemistry: Analysis of Composition, Chemical Bonding, and Electronic Structure of Surfaces and Interfaces. In: Methods in Physical Chemistry. Wiley-VCH Verlag GmbH & Co. KGaA, Weinheim, Germany, pp 477–512

91. Beck S (2014) Untersuchung des Ladungstransfers in organischen Halbleitern mit in-situ Infrarotspektroskopie. University of Heidelberg

92. Brauer JC, Lee YH, Nazeeruddin MK, Banerji N (2016) Ultrafast charge carrier dynamics in CH 3 NH 3 PbI 3 : evidence for hot hole injection into spiro-OMeTAD. J Mater Chem C 4:5922–5931. https://doi.org/10.1039/C6TC00763E

93. Kaelble DH (1970) Dispersion-Polar Surface Tension Properties of Organic Solids. J Adhes 2:66–81. https://doi.org/10.1080/00218467708544582

94. Ruscello M, Sarkar T, Levitsky A, et al (2019) Nanocomposite of Nickel Oxide Nanoparticles and Polyethylene Oxide as Printable Hole Transport Layer for Organic Solar Cells. Sustain Energy Fuels. https://doi.org/10.1039/C9SE00216B

95. Ruscello M, Stolz S, Gonzalez Arellano DL, et al (2017) Electron injection and interfacial trap passivation in solution-processed organic light-emitting diodes using a polymer zwitterion interlayer. Org Electron 50:384–388. https://doi.org/10.1016/j.orgel.2017.08.014

96. Raupp S, Daume D, Tekoglu S, et al (2016) Slot Die Coated and Flexo Printed Highly Efficient SMOLEDs. Adv Mater Technol 1600230. https://doi.org/10.1002/admt.201600230

97. Hernandez-Sosa G, Bornemann N, Ringle I, et al (2013) Rheological and drying considerations for uniformly gravure-printed layers: Towards large-area flexible organic light-emitting diodes. Adv Funct Mater 23:3164–3171. https://doi.org/10.1002/adfm.201202862

98. Stolz S, Petzoldt M, Dück S, et al (2016) High-Performance Electron Injection Layers with a Wide Processing Window from an Amidoamine-Functionalized Polyfluorene. ACS Appl Mater

Interfaces 8:12959–12967.
https://doi.org/10.1021/acsami.6b03557

99. Choy WCH, Zhang D (2016) Solution-Processed Metal Oxides as Efficient Carrier Transport Layers for Organic Photovoltaics. Small 12:416–431. https://doi.org/10.1002/smll.201502258

100. Wang F, Tan Z, Li Y (2015) Solution-processable metal oxides/chelates as electrode buffer layers for efficient and stable polymer solar cells. Energy Environ Sci 8:1059–1091. https://doi.org/10.1039/c4ee03802a

101. Sun C, Wu Z, Yip HL, et al (2016) Amino-Functionalized Conjugated Polymer as an Efficient Electron Transport Layer for High-Performance Planar-Heterojunction Perovskite Solar Cells. Adv Energy Mater 6:1–10. https://doi.org/10.1002/aenm.201501534

102. Kim O, Kang B, Lee J, et al (2016) Efficient Quantum Dots Light-Emitting Devices Using Polyvinyl Pyrrolidone-Capped ZnO Nanoparticles With Enhanced Charge Transport. IEEE Electron Device Lett 37:1022–1024

103. Wang J, Lin K, Zhang K, et al (2016) Crosslinkable Amino-Functionalized Conjugated Polymer as Cathode Interlayer for Efficient Inverted Polymer Solar Cells. Adv Energy Mater 6:. https://doi.org/10.1002/aenm.201502563

104. Huang F, Wu H, Cao Y (2010) Water/alcohol soluble conjugated polymers as highly efficient electron transporting/injection layer in optoelectronic devices. Chem Soc Rev 39:2500–2521. https://doi.org/10.1039/b907991m

105. Page ZA, Duzhko V V., Emrick T (2013) Conjugated thiophene-containing polymer zwitterions: Direct synthesis and thin film electronic properties. Macromolecules 46:344–351. https://doi.org/10.1021/ma302232q

106. Liu Y, Duzhko V V, Page ZA, et al (2016) Conjugated Polymer Zwitterions: Efficient Interlayer Materials in Organic Electronics. Acc Chem Res 49:2478–2488. https://doi.org/10.1021/acs.accounts.6b00402

107. Fang J, Wallikewitz BH, Gao F, et al (2011) Conjugated

zwitterionic polyelectrolyte as the charge injection layer for high-performance polymer light-emitting diodes. J Am Chem Soc 133:683–685. https://doi.org/10.1021/ja108541z

108.   Zhang W, Song C, Liu X, Fang J (2016) Realizing Highly Efficient Inverted Photovoltaic Cells by Combination of Nonconjugated Small-Molecule Zwitterions with Polyethylene Glycol. ACS Appl Mater Interfaces 8:18593–18599. https://doi.org/10.1021/acsami.6b04955

109.   Duan C, Wang L, Zhang K, et al (2011) Conjugated zwitterionic polyelectrolytes and their neutral precursor as electron injection layer for high-performance polymer light-emitting diodes. Adv Mater 23:1665–1669. https://doi.org/10.1002/adma.201004661

110.   Islam A, Li J, Pervaiz M, et al (2019) Zwitterions for Organic/Perovskite Solar Cells, Light-Emitting Devices, and Lithium Ion Batteries: Recent Progress and Perspectives. Adv Energy Mater 9:1–35. https://doi.org/10.1002/aenm.201803354

111.   Beane GA, Morfa AJ, Funston AM, Mulvaney P (2012) Defect-mediated energy transfer between ZnO nanocrystals and a conjugated dye. J Phys Chem C 116:3305–3310. https://doi.org/10.1021/jp209638g

112.   Morfa AJ, Macdonald BI, Subbiah J, Jasieniak JJ (2014) Understanding the chemical origin of improved thin-film device performance from photodoped ZnO nanoparticles. Sol Energy Mater Sol Cells 124:211–216. https://doi.org/10.1016/j.solmat.2014.02.002

113.   Koga O, Onishi T, Tamaru K (1980) Adsorption and decomposition of isopropyl alcohol over zinc oxide. Infrared and kinetic study. J Chem Soc Faraday Trans 1 Phys Chem Condens Phases 76:19. https://doi.org/10.1039/f19807600019

114.   Noei H, Wöll C, Muhler M, Wang Y (2011) Activation of Carbon Dioxide on ZnO Nanoparticles Studied by Vibrational Spectroscopy. J Phys Chem C 115:908–914. https://doi.org/10.1021/jp102751t

115. Ashkenov N, Mbenkum BN, Bundesmann C, et al (2003) Infrared dielectric functions and phonon modes of high-quality ZnO films. J Appl Phys 93:126–133. https://doi.org/10.1063/1.1526935

116. Greiner MT, Helander MG, Wang Z Bin, et al (2010) Effects of processing conditions on the work function and energy-level alignment of NiO thin films. J Phys Chem C 114:19777–19781. https://doi.org/10.1021/jp108281m

117. Hietzschold S, Hillebrandt S, Ullrich F, et al (2017) Functionalized Nickel Oxide Hole Contact Layers: Work Function versus Conductivity. ACS Appl Mater Interfaces 9:39821–39829. https://doi.org/10.1021/acsami.7b12784

118. Ullrich F, Hillebrandt S, Hietzschold S, et al (2018) Correlation between Chemical and Electronic Properties of Solution-Processed Nickel Oxide. ACS Appl Energy Mater 1:3113–3122. https://doi.org/10.1021/acsaem.8b00284

119. Hou Y, Chen W, Baran D, et al (2016) Overcoming the Interface Losses in Planar Heterojunction Perovskite-Based Solar Cells. Adv Mater 5112–5120. https://doi.org/10.1002/adma.201504168

120. Yang W, Yu Z, Liu W, et al (2017) Aqueous solution-processed NiO $_x$ anode buffer layers applicable for polymer solar cells. J Polym Sci Part A Polym Chem 55:747–753. https://doi.org/10.1002/pola.28427

121. Jiang F, Choy WCH, Li X, et al (2015) Post-treatment-free solution-processed Non-stoichiometric NiO<inf>x</inf> nanoparticles for efficient hole-transport layers of organic optoelectronic devices. Adv Mater 27:2930–2937. https://doi.org/10.1002/adma.201405391

122. Wei Y, Yao K, Wang X, et al (2018) Improving the efficiency and environmental stability of inverted planar perovskite solar cells via silver-doped nickel oxide hole-transporting layer. Appl Surf Sci 427:782–790. https://doi.org/10.1016/j.apsusc.2017.08.184

123. Ratcliff EL, Meyer J, Steirer KX, et al (2011) Evidence for near-Surface NiOOH Species in Solution-Processed NiO x Selective

Interlayer Materials: Impact on Energetics and the Performance of Polymer Bulk Heterojunction Photovoltaics. Chem Mater 23:4988–5000. https://doi.org/10.1021/cm202296p

124.   Hu H, Zhu J, Chen M, et al (2018) Inkjet-printed p-type nickel oxide thin-film transistor. Appl Surf Sci 441:295–302. https://doi.org/10.1016/j.apsusc.2018.02.049

125.   Brisse R, Faddoul R, Bourgeteau T, et al (2017) Inkjet printing NiO-based p-Type dye-sensitized solar cells. ACS Appl Mater Interfaces 9:2369–2377. https://doi.org/10.1021/acsami.6b12912

126.   Singh A, Gupta SK, Garg A (2017) Inkjet printing of NiO films and integration as hole transporting layers in polymer solar cells. Sci Rep 7:1775. https://doi.org/10.1038/s41598-017-01897-9

127.   Mustafa B, Griffin J, Alsulami AS, et al (2014) Solution processed nickel oxide anodes for organic photovoltaic devices. Appl Phys Lett 104:6–11. https://doi.org/10.1063/1.4865090

128.   Zhang H, Cheng J, Lin F, et al (2016) Pinhole-free and surface-nanostructured niox film by room-Temperature solution process for high-performance flexible perovskite solar cells with good stability and reproducibility. ACS Nano 10:1503–1511. https://doi.org/10.1021/acsnano.5b07043

129.   Wang K-C, Jeng J-Y, Shen P-S, et al (2014) p-type Mesoscopic Nickel Oxide/Organometallic Perovskite Heterojunction Solar Cells. Sci Rep 4:4756. https://doi.org/10.1038/srep04756

130.   Chen HL, Lu YM, Hwang WS (2005) Characterization of sputtered NiO thin films. Surf Coatings Technol 198:138–142. https://doi.org/10.1016/j.surfcoat.2004.10.032

131.   Zhang J, Wang J, Fu Y, et al (2014) Efficient and stable polymer solar cells with annealing-free solution-processible NiO nanoparticles as anode buffer layers. J Mater Chem C 2:8295–8302. https://doi.org/10.1039/C4TC01302F

132.   Kwon U, Kim B-G, Nguyen DC, et al (2016) Solution-Processible Crystalline NiO Nanoparticles for High-Performance Planar Perovskite Photovoltaic Cells. Sci Rep 6:30759.

https://doi.org/10.1038/srep30759

133. Small CE, Chen S, Subbiah J, et al (2012) High-efficiency inverted dithienogermole-thienopyrrolodione-based polymer solar cells. Nat Photonics 6:115–120. https://doi.org/10.1038/nphoton2011317

134. Jlassi M, Sta I, Hajji M, Ezzaouia H (2014) Optical and electrical properties of nickel oxide thin films synthesized by sol-gel spin coating. Mater Sci Semicond Process 21:7–13. https://doi.org/10.1016/j.mssp.2014.01.018

135. Marsh RA, Hodgkiss JM, Albert-Seifried S, Friend RH (2010) Effect of Annealing on P3HT:PCBM Charge Transfer and Nanoscale Morphology Probed by Ultrafast Spectroscopy. Nano Lett 10:923–930. https://doi.org/10.1021/nl9038289

136. Howard IA, Mauer R, Meister M, Laquai F (2010) Effect of Morphology on Ultrafast Free Carrier Generation in Polythiophene:Fullerene Organic Solar Cells. J Am Chem Soc 132:14866–14876. https://doi.org/10.1021/ja105260d

137. Banerji N, Cowan S, Vauthey E, Heeger AJ (2011) Ultrafast Relaxation of the Poly(3-hexylthiophene) Emission Spectrum. J Phys Chem C 115:9726–9739. https://doi.org/10.1021/jp1119348

138. Cook S, Furube A, Katoh R (2008) Analysis of the excited states of regioregular polythiophene P3HT. Energy Environ Sci 1:294. https://doi.org/10.1039/b805643a

139. Stolz S, Scherer M, Mankel E, et al (2014) Investigation of solution-processed Ultrathin electron injection layers for organic light-emitting diodes. ACS Appl Mater Interfaces 6:6616–6622. https://doi.org/10.1021/am500287y

140. Courtright BAE, Jenekhe SA (2015) Polyethylenimine Interfacial Layers in Inverted Organic Photovoltaic Devices: Effects of Ethoxylation and Molecular Weight on Efficiency and Temporal Stability. ACS Appl Mater Interfaces 7:26167–26175. https://doi.org/10.1021/acsami.5b08147

141. Kang H, Hong S, Lee J, Lee K (2012) Electrostatically Self-Assembled Nonconjugated Polyelectrolytes as an Ideal

Interfacial Layer for Inverted Polymer Solar Cells. Adv Mater 24:3005–3009. https://doi.org/10.1002/adma.201200594

142.   Jia X, Wu N, Wei J, et al (2016) A low-cost and low-temperature processable zinc oxide-polyethylenimine (ZnO:PEI) nanocomposite as cathode buffer layer for organic and perovskite solar cells. Org Electron 38:150–157. https://doi.org/10.1016/j.orgel.2016.08.012

143.   Snedden EWW, Cury LAA, Bourdakos KNN, Monkman APP (2010) High photoluminescence quantum yield due to intramolecular energy transfer in the Super Yellow conjugated copolymer. Chem Phys Lett 490:76–79. https://doi.org/10.1016/j.cplett.2010.03.030

144.   Zhou H, Zhang Y, Seifter J, et al (2013) High-efficiency polymer solar cells enhanced by solvent treatment. Adv Mater 25:1646–1652. https://doi.org/10.1002/adma.201204306

145.   Han NS, Shim HS, Seo JH, et al (2010) Defect states of ZnO nanoparticles: Discrimination by time-resolved photoluminescence spectroscopy. J Appl Phys 107:. https://doi.org/10.1063/1.3382915

146.   Hassan MU, Liu YC, Hasan KU, et al (2016) Charge trap assisted high efficiency in new polymer-blend based light emitting diodes. Nano Energy 21:62–70. https://doi.org/10.1016/j.nanoen.2015.12.023

147.   Wu WT, Hsu CM, Lin WM, et al (2016) Optical effects of NiOxinterlayer for OLEDs with AZO embedded anodes. Mater Chem Phys 183:405–409. https://doi.org/10.1016/j.matchemphys.2016.08.045

148.   Woo S, Kim J, Cho G, et al (2009) Influence of nickel oxide nanolayer and doping in organic light-emitting devices. J Ind Eng Chem 15:716–718. https://doi.org/10.1016/j.jiec.2009.09.051

149.   Kim J, Park HJ, Grigoropoulos CP, et al (2016) Solution-processed nickel oxide nanoparticles with NiOOH for hole injection layers of high-efficiency organic light-emitting diodes. Nanoscale 17608–17615. https://doi.org/10.1039/C6NR04643F

150.   Jankus V, Snedden EW, Bright DW, et al (2013) Energy
        Upconversion via Triplet Fusion in Super Yellow PPV Films
        Doped with Palladium Tetraphenyltetrabenzoporphyrin: a
        Comprehensive Investigation of Exciton Dynamics. Adv Funct
        Mater 23:384–393. https://doi.org/10.1002/adfm.201201284

151.   Causa M, De Jonghe-Risse J, Scarongella M, et al (2016) The fate
        of electron-hole pairs in polymer:fullerene blends for organic
        photovoltaics. Nat Commun 7:.
        https://doi.org/10.1038/ncomms12556

152.   Krauspe P, Tsokkou D, Causa' M, et al (2018) Terahertz short-
        range mobilities in neat and intermixed regions of
        polymer:fullerene blends with controlled phase morphology. J
        Mater Chem A 6:22301–22309.
        https://doi.org/10.1039/C8TA08061E

153.   Antohe S, Iftimie S, Hrostea L, et al (2017) A critical review of
        photovoltaic cells based on organic monomeric and polymeric
        thin film heterojunctions. Thin Solid Films 642:219–231.
        https://doi.org/10.1016/j.tsf.2017.09.041

154.   Nelson J (2011) Polymer:fullerene bulk heterojunction solar
        cells. Mater Today 14:462–470.
        https://doi.org/10.1016/S1369-7021(11)70210-3

155.   Zuo L, Yao J, Li H, Chen H (2014) Assessing the origin of the S-
        shaped I-V curve in organic solar cells: An improved equivalent
        circuit model. Sol Energy Mater Sol Cells 122:88–93.
        https://doi.org/10.1016/j.solmat.2013.11.018

156.   Wang JC, Ren XC, Shi SQ, et al (2011) Charge accumulation
        induced S-shape J-V curves in bilayer heterojunction organic
        solar cells. Org Electron physics, Mater Appl 12:880–885.
        https://doi.org/10.1016/j.orgel.2011.02.016

157.   Peng B, Guo X, Zou Y, et al (2011) Performance improvement of
        annealing-free P3HT : PCBM-based polymer solar cells via 3-
        methylthiophene additive. J Phys D Appl Phys 44:365101.
        https://doi.org/10.1088/0022-3727/44/36/365101

Acknowledgements

I would like to thank all the people who have accompanied and supported me in various ways over the past years and who have contributed to the successful conclusion of this thesis.

A heartfelt thanks to **Prof. Wolfgang Kowalsky** and to **Luat Nguyen**: thank you for enabling me to work in InnovationLab and to complete my doctorate at TU Braunschweig, and for always providing me with trustworthy advice and support.

My biggest thanks go to my direct scientific supervisor **Dr. Gerardo Hernandez-Sosa** for supporting me during these years. Thank you for the inspiration, the mentoring, the many scientific discussions as well as your untired help regarding my publications and my thesis. Thanks for showing me the tips and tricks of scientific writing, of presentations, and how to navigate through scientific networks without getting intimidated. And besides that, I thank you for the great trust (and patience) you have placed in me at all times.

I am very grateful to **the ITN-INFORM organization and management** panel, for realizing such a grand project, giving me the opportunity to do my doctorate in such an exciting network and to attend so many interesting workshops and conferences, to establish collaborations and most importantly the possibility to travel for research stays by the different partners. Thank you to **all my fellow Early Stage Researchers** for the inspiring ideas and the good company during the many meetings around.

In particular, thanks to **Prof. Natalie Banerji, Prof. Natalie Stingelin** and to **Prof. Gitti L. Frey** for proofreading my publication and letting me spend the unforgettable months as a visiting researcher in your research groups. I thank you very much for all your support, and for being an inspiration as great scientists and great women.

A big thank you to **Prof. Natalie Banerji** and her whole group, especially to **Nikos**, for the scientific help that I received from you, for proof-reading my thesis as well as the nice time I spent with you in Fribourg and in Bern.

A big thank you to the people in Imperial College London from Prof. Natalie Stingelin's group, especially **Gianmaria** and **Matt,** for the scientific help and for the fun, you helped making my three months in London memorable.

A big thank you to the whole group of Prof. Gitti Frey, especially to **Tanmoy** and to **Artem**, for staying late for the experiments and for showing me around in Haifa.

My sincere thanks go to **all group members of the LTI** at InnovationLab. Thank you for adopting me, for your scientific support, for the many fun activities and a great time together. In this context, I would like to emphasize **Gerardo, Stefan, Nils, Tobi, Noah, Martin, Jozi, Manu, Mervin** and from the earlier times **Ralph, Sebastian, Anthony, Flo** who have accompanied my path in the KIT group over these years. I still wish that at least one of you was a girl, for a bit of variety. In particular, thank you **Stefan** for being my favorite crankiest desk neighbor and for teaching me a bit of inkjet printing.

I would also like to thank **all the employees of InnovationLab GmbH**. Thank you very much for the time and effort you put into running the site. The working conditions here are really excellent and I hope that the location will continue to develop as positively as in recent years. In particular, thanks to **Hildegard** for the patience and for the helping me navigate the bureaucracy.

I would also like to thank all employees and students of the other partners represented at the site for their scientific support and helpfulness over the past years. In particular, thanks to **Florian** and to **Patrick** for the help with the photoelectron spectroscopy and thanks to **Sabina** for the help with the infrared measurements.

A thank you to my life-long friends back in Italy: **Laura, Andrea, Margherita, Lucie**, thanks for always make me laugh and remember that somewhere I have a happy island.

I dedicate this thesis to my childhood cat and life-long friend, **Gatto**, who after 19 years passed away this January. You'll live in my memory and as my desktop background, the thing I look at the most.

Last but not least, I would like to express all my gratitude to my parents **Jutta** and **Giancarlo** and to my sister **Sara**. Over the years you have always supported me in the best way possible and have always been one hundred percent there for me. That's how you made my studies and this doctorate possible in the first place. Thank you.

Herstellung und Verlag:
BoD – Books on Demand, Norderstedt
ISBN: 978-3-7386-4652-8

Ingram Content Group UK Ltd.
Milton Keynes UK
UKHW020747280323
419292UK00015B/543